Kenneth

IN THE
BLEAK
MIDWINTER

NICK HERN BOOKS
London

A Nick Hern Book

In the Bleak Midwinter first published in Great Britain in 1995
as an original paperback by Nick Hern Books Ltd,
14 Larden Road, London W3 7ST

In the Bleak Midwinter screenplay and introduction
copyright © 1995 by Kenneth Branagh Ltd

Film stills and front cover photo
copyright © 1995 by Castle Rock Entertainment

Photos by David Appleby

Kenneth Branagh has asserted his moral right to be identified
as the author of this work

Lines from 'Why Must the Show Go On' by Noël Coward
copyright © 1950 the Estate of Noël Coward

Lines from 'Heart of Glass' (Deborah Harry and Chris Stein),
published by Chrysalis Music Inc.

Typeset by Country Setting, Woodchurch, Kent TN26 3TB
Printed and bound by Cox & Wyman Ltd, Reading, Berks RG1 8EX

A CIP catalogue record for this book is available from
the British Library.

ISBN 1 85459 269 6

Introduction

'Comedy is a very serious business', said David Garrick (among others).

My experience in the theatre is that comedy also springs *from* very serious business. The more 'serious' the play the more likely rehearsals are to create amusement, not always intentional, not always enjoyed by the people involved. In Shakespeare particularly, the great tragedies tread such a fine line between laughter and tears, that any group working on them can find themselves in the grip of hysteria. Especially if, as is often the case, time is short. It means that relationships between actors, directors, stage-managers, designers – the ad hoc 'family' that is a theatrical company – become very intense. Angry showdowns, love affairs, nervous collapses, philosophical breakthroughs can all occur in a frighteningly short space of time.

It's the very stuff of drama, inside the drama. The stakes are even higher when the people involved have invested themselves, personally and financially, in the show. Then, desperation is added to the mix. The agony increases as does the laughter.

I wanted to write something about what I'd observed of this over fifteen years as an actor. Taking Mr Garrick's clue, I attempted to make my departure point a serious one. At the heart of the film I wanted to touch on the personal lives of the characters involved. The actors' melancholy, loneliness and isolation. Their ongoing, relationship with failure, rejection and humiliation. Familiar feelings to many people but often concentrated in the lives of actors. Around this desire to observe human nature in absurd crisis, I tried to build the comedy. For my prime aim was to make people laugh.

The theatre as a metaphor for life's madness is hardly new. And movies that use the stories of particular productions to provide a microcosmic view of human nature abound. The 'backstage' drama is almost a genre. I grew up watching them on television – Mickey Rooney and Judy Garland in *Babes in Arms* – 'Why: we could do the show right here,' they proclaimed, and then promptly gave us a dozen complicated dance numbers featuring thousands of people (all in the school gymnasium), which they couldn't possibly have had time to rehearse. I marvelled at it. There was Warner Baxter yelling at Ruby Keeler in *42nd Street* and Jack Benny farcing his way through a Nazi-infested Hamlet in *To Be Or Not To Be.*

They had the magic of black and white photography. The sense of a heightened reality which seems to fit when describing the world of the theatre. But these movies talked of Broadway and other exotic locations. The shows involved were musicals.

My most regular theatrical experiences, by comparison, have been low-budget Shakespeares in places like Norwich (in a tent, incidentally). But that was partly the point, I suppose. This could be the farty British version, with its roots much more firmly in the soil of the Ealing Comedy tradition. The aspirations of the characters seem to remain the same regardless of the locale.

I wanted in any case, to use something as famous and dangerously cliché-ridden as *Hamlet*, for the show within the show. It's a play which has obsessed me for the last twenty years, and one that most people have been exposed to in some form or other. Either in some misty cultural memory of a man in black tights with a skull or through TV advertisements for small cigars that bear the same name. It represents, for some, Shakespeare's greatest achievement, and for others its meaning is as remote as an ancient civilisation. One of the characters asks how a fourteen-year-old in 1995 can connect or identify in any way with a four hundred-year-old play about a depressed aristocrat. I've spent most of my career trying to answer the same question.

So is this screenplay pure autobiography? Well, I don't think so. It's certainly very personal. There is much of me in Joe (although not the terrible experience of a year's unemployment), but as the screenplay developed it started to belong to the actors involved.

I wrote it with many of them in mind, and once they were officially cast their contribution was enormous. It was the cumulative experience of this group that informed and changed the script. All the mad audition sequences come from life, as do many of the characters. The film itself was made in the spirit of the story. Everyone – actors and crew – received the same initial payment, and everyone who worked throughout the shoot receives a profit participation. The very fact of this affected the tone of the final movie. The spirit of generous collaboration (not without the odd fit of temper) made for a shoot (of just twenty-one days) which, as Hamlet would say, held 'the mirror up to nature'.

The gap between life and art in this case was quite narrow. At times it made for an atmosphere of utter silliness, which anyone who passionately believes in the power of the theatre is also equally familiar with.

The ending takes us into different territory. Some will find it sentimental. It is. Actors are sentimental. It's one of our weaknesses. But I believe at times one of the gloriously silly ones. It may not translate into action on all occasions. Or overcome the vanity, greed and insecurity to which we are regularly and comically prey, but in this instance I wanted the happy ending, which us beggarly actors so long for, and rarely find.

I hope that elsewhere there is enough of the bitter irony which constitutes much of the actor's life to earn us our fictional place in the winter sun. For if this is a true valentine to the theatre and actors, it should be shot through with the (albeit unheroic) pain of the process. That was our serious intent in the business of this comedy, aimed above all at giving pleasure.

My everlasting thanks to the talented and kind group of collaborators who allowed me to have a go.

Kenneth Branagh

For
David Barron, Tim Harvey, Iona Price,
Tamar Thomas and Terry Pritchard

Midwinter Films

in association with

Castle Rock Entertainment

A Kenneth Branagh Film

IN THE BLEAK MIDWINTER

Starring in alphabetical order

Richard Briers	Gerard Horan
Hetta Charnley	Celia Imrie
Joan Collins	Michael Maloney
Nicholas Farrell	Julia Sawalha
Mark Hadfield	John Sessions

with

Jennifer Saunders

Ann Davies

Robert Hines

James D White

Music by Jimmy Yuill

Costume Designer Caroline Harris

Editor Neil Farrell

Director of Photography Roger Lanser

Production Designer Tim Harvey

Associate Producers Iona Price and Tamar Thomas

Produced by David Barron

Written and Directed by Kenneth Branagh

'Dylan Judd…? But he's… he's… he's short.'

Joe (Michael Maloney) dealing with his reaction to a
successful rival. Margaretta (Joan Collins) is amused.

'I feel something very powerful and strange.'

Fadge (Celia Imrie) taking in the atmosphere of the church.

The Company 'Warm-up.'

'You won't fail.'

Says Nina (Julia Sawalha).
Joe (Michael Maloney) is not so sure.

'Can I just mention smoking?'

Tom (Nicholas Farrell) makes an unpopular remark to a
nervous company at the start of the read through.

'It's a bit limp.'

Joe (Michael Maloney) inspires Carnforth (Gerard Horan)
to produce fear as Bernardo.

*'Do you intend anyone to come
and see this boss?'*

enquires Vernon (Mark Hadfield).
Molly (Hetta Charnley) muses over the box office charts.

'I'm… I'm… speechless.'

Joe (Michael Maloney) is shocked at the success of the final
run-through. Nina (Julia Sawalha) always knew it would work.

'Not bad, eh love?'

Henry (Richard Briers) and Terry (John Sessions)
reveal their 'look'. Nina (Julia Sawalha) and
Vernon (Mark Hadfield) say nothing.

'I promise it will be marvellous dahling.'

A nervous Margaretta (Joan Collins)
persuades Nancy (Jennifer Saunders).

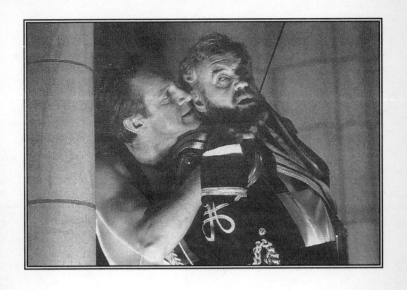

The Performance 'Give me my father'

Tom (Nicholas Farrell) gives us his Laertes
to Henry's (Richard Briers) Claudius.

Nancy (Jennifer Saunders) finds her Smegma.
And Tom (Nicholas Farrell) finds a new agent.

IN THE BLEAK MIDWINTER

Cast

HENRY	Richard Briers
MOLLY	Hetta Charnley
MARGARETTA	Joan Collins
TOM	Nicholas Farrell
VERNON	Mark Hadfield
CARNFORTH	Gerard Horan
FADGE	Celia Imrie
JOE	Michael Maloney
NANCY CRAWFORD	Jennifer Saunders
NINA	Julia Sawalha
TERRY	John Sessions
MRS BRANCH	Ann Davies
TIM	James D. White
MORTIMER	Robert Hines
TAP DANCER	Allie Byrne
PUPPET WOMAN	Katy Carmichael
YOUNG ACTOR	Adrian Scarborough
VENTRILOQUIST	Brian Petifer
SCOTSMAN	Patrick Doyle
MULE TRAIN MAN	Shaun Prendergast
AUDIENCE MEMBER	Carol Starks
NINA'S FATHER	Edward Jewesbury

Black.

The credits dissolve slowly on and off as we hear the unmistakable voice of Noël Coward.

The world for some years
Has been sodden with tears
On behalf of the acting profession.

Each star
Playing a part
Seems to expect
A purple heart.

It's unorthodox
To be born in a box
But it needn't become an obsession.

Let's hope we have no more to plague us
Than three shows a night in Las Vegas.

When I think of physicians
And mathematicians
Who don't earn a quart of the dough
When I think of the miners
And waiters in diners
There's one thing I'm burning to know . . .

> *But before we can launch into the jaunty chorus,*
>
> *Cut.*

1   INT. – DAY.

> *Mid-shot on* JOE *who speaks directly to camera. He is of medium height, dark, wiry.*

JOE. It was late November, er . . . I think . . . and I was thinking about the whole Christmas thing, the birth of Christ, Wizard of Oz, family murders, and quite frankly I was depressed. I mean I'd always wanted to live my life like in an old movie – a sort of fairytale you know? Mind you, I suppose if you think that a lot of fairytales turn out to be nightmares, and that a lot of old movies are crap, then that's what I did. Er, the thing was, you know the way doctors say that nervous breakdowns can happen, very fast and dramatically; sort of big bang, or, there are the other kind that happen very slowly, over a period of time. Well I was thirty-three years old, this one started when I was about seven months, and it had just begun to get a grip . . .

> *Cut.*

> *Mr Coward's chorus lines finally begin as the remaining CREDITS roll swiftly, white on black. The last disappears and a legend proclaims:*

PROLOGUE

'I HAVE TO TALK TO MY AGENT'

2   INT. RESTAURANT – DAY.

> *Mid-heated conversation between* JOE *and his agent* MARGARETTA D'ARVILLE, *laconic, smart dressing: part agent, part therapist.*

MARGARETTA. Darling. You're depressed that's all, everyone gets depressed. For most people, there's no happy, there's no sad, there's just various stages of depressed. That's life.

JOE. Well, not for me. Not anymore. Look, please help me with this idea.

MARGARETTA. Darling, you tried it before. It was a disaster.

JOE. Margy, I've been an actor now for eleven years. If everything had gone according to Laurence Olivier's book I would have known triumph, disappointment and married a beautiful woman. Instead I've known tedium, humiliation and got shacked up with the psycho from hell. Life has to change.

MARGARETTA. But not by committing professional suicide.

JOE. I have to do this play. I've given my life a deadline.

MARGARETTA. Look it's Christmas, wait till the New Year, give it some thought.

JOE. I have given it thought, 365 days' worth.

> *Cut.*

2

3 EXT. STREET – DAY.

> *A busy London thoroughfare.* MARGARETTA *and* JOE
> *are walking towards us. Talking across each other.*

MARGARETTA. Alright, you get the £600 and my office and a
phone for one week. Now, I want to be in on the casting. You can
put an ad in Theatre Weekly, but you better be careful we don't
want law suits. And I'm warning you, at this time of year, everyone is doing Christmas shows or TV specials so all you are going
to get are eccentrics, misfits and nutters.

JOE. Margy, I love you.

> JOE *kisses* MARGARETTA.

MARGARETTA. Oh shush you silly little suicidal megalomaniac.

JOE. Margy, Margy, what about that film?

MARGARETTA. What film?

JOE. That stupid science-fiction film.

MARGARETTA. Ah yes, you said you weren't interested in that!

JOE. I'm just curious.

MARGARETTA. Well . . . it was down to you and Dylan Judd.

> *Pause.*

JOE. Dylan J . . . I don't believe it . . . I don't . . . I'm . . . I'm, I'm
speechless . . . I'm

MARGARETTA (*putting on her sunglasses*). I'm so glad, I'm so
glad you've regained your artistic soul darling, I really am. You
mustn't let these little things bother you. .

> *She goes. He remains spluttering.*

JOE. Dylan Judd . . . Dylan Judd . . . he's . . . he's short . . .

> *Cut.*

4 EXT. NEWSAGENTS. DAY.

> JOE *dashes out of the shop, clutching his copy of* Theatre
> Weekly.

> MARGARETTA *is waiting in her Land Rover to review
> the ad.* JOE *clambers into the passenger seat.*

3

JOE (*pointing out the ad*). There, there.

MARGARETTA (*reading*). AUDITIONS . . . nice and big that's good. LIMITED ENGAGEMENT, DEC 11TH – DEC 31ST, HAMLET . . . that's clear, simple, so far so good . . . A CO-OPERATIVE EXPERIENCE . . . do you have to use these phrases darling, it's not 1969 . . .

JOE. . . . People need to know it's an ensemble . . .

MARGARETTA. . . . and that you're the biggest ensembler . . .

JOE. . . . get on with it . . . Please, please.

MARGARETTA(*appalled*). . . . PROFIT-SHARE, 'SPIRIT SHARE' . . . unbelievable.

JOE. . . . it's not about money . . .

MARGARETTA. . . . or grammar . . . ACCOMMODATION AND 'INSPIRATION' . . . can't you just say their digs are included . . .

JOE.. . . . They need to recognize the commitment . . .

MARGARETTA. . . . what's this . . . oh God . . . 'SIX FELLOW JOURNEYMEN TO ENTER THE GLOOMY DANE' . . .

JOE. Oh no . . . That's a mistake . . . No, no it should be to 'To Enter the *World* Of The Gloomy Dane . . . '

MARGARETTA. . . . It hardly matters darling . . . it finishes with . . . APPLY TO THE DIRECTOR AND SWEAT PRINCE . . .

JOE. . . . *Sweet*, sweet, sweet prince . . .

MARGARETTA. Great darling. Expect a lot of new-age gays looking for a workout.

> *Cut.*

Caption white on black:

ACT I

'WHY . . . WE COULD DO THE SHOW RIGHT HERE'

5 INT. AGENT'S OFFICE – DAY.

> *Close-up on JOE, sitting behind a desk. Music plays through the following audition montage, which begins with JOE, unused to this position of power, nervous and*

4

eager. Desperate to make his fellows comfortable. His wide-eyed and optimistic expression changes markedly as the succession of candidates passes before him through the tiny, anonymous office.

MARGARETTA *sits in the office throughout.*

JOE. It's terrific that you could come in . . . thanks very much indeed. Now this is a really collaborative piece but . . . if you'd . . . like to do something, it doesn't have to be Shakespeare . . . you know . . . whatever . . . this production wants to be extremely innovative in the way we communicate . . .

We cut to a lycra-ed woman tap dancer who smiles a cheesy, face-splitting grin on the other side of the desk. A string around her neck holding flip-over cards which she turns as she taps. Flip. The card reads 'THIS IS TO BE OR NOT TO BE'. *She taps,*

JOE (*genuinely amazed*). Ah . . . Ah . . . Ah . . . Ah . . .

TAP DANCER (*delighted*). Thanks, I thought it would probably work.

MARGARETTA *in shock.*

Cut.

Close-up on the contorted face of a young actor in hunch-back mode giving the full dalek-ian version of Olivier's Richard III.

YOUNG ACTOR. 'Now is the winter of our discontent Made glorious summer by this son of York.'

JOE (*rushing to the actor, all concern*). I don't feel you've made it quite your own, you know . . . Listen, let's just drop the voice, silly idea I know, and drop the hunch and the gestures OK?

YOUNG ACTOR (*eager*). OK. Fine.

JOE *goes back to his desk.*

JOE. Then let's just see what happens. Whenever you want, in your own time.

After great loosening-up preparations. He does it exactly the same way.

YOUNG ACTOR. 'Now is the winter of our discontent Made glorious summer by this son of York.'

JOE *ushers him out.*

JOE. Absolute transformation.

YOUNG ACTOR. Oh, it felt great . . .

JOE. Thank you, thank you so much.

YOUNG ACTOR. It was like something really freed up.

JOE. You did, you freed right up.

> *Cut.*

> *Close up on* HENRY WAKEFIELD, *been there, seen that, done it all, liked none of it type, loves the theatre and acting in spite of himself. The child of an older school he's a decrepit cross between Henry Irving and Tony Hancock. He drags heavily on a roll-up.*

HENRY WAKEFIELD. Henry Wakefield's the name love, known as Harry to those who wish to annoy me.

JOE. Whatever you prefer to be . . .

HENRY. Look love, I won't mess about. I hate these profit-share things. I want to play the King, right. I should have played it years ago but you's pays your money and puts up with your miserable bloody choices.

JOE. Yes. Well it's a wonderful role –

HENRY. Less of the director bullshit love – just say yes. Let's face it you're lucky to have me. From your ad this production's already about as promising as playing *Rookery Nook* on the Titanic, so don't waste my time sonny eh?

See you at the read-through.

> *Cut.*

> *Close up on* HENRY WAKEFIELD's *ancient, glamourised oddly-angled* Spotlight *photo, being pinned to a wall with his assigned character names below it – Claudius, Ghost, Player-King.*

> *Cut*

> *to Ultra Variety type Ventriloquist and dummy, hard to tell them apart. Both sound like a strangulated Tommy Cooper.*

DUMMY. . . . . alas, poor Yorick, I knew him well.

> *Cut.*

> *To* MARGARETTA *miming 'no' and 'he's mad'.*

6

DUMMY (*insane*). He likes us, he likes us, he thinks we're funny . . .

> *Cut.*

> *The face of an intense young actor,* TOM NEWMAN. *Vegetarian, Planet-saving, Whale-rescuing, Trade-papers reading and, finally and conclusively, self-absorbed. He is in earnest flow, despite being intellectually challenged.*

TOM. . . but no, no, no, no, Hamlet isn't just Hamlet, oh no, no, oh no, Hamlet is me . . . Hamlet is . . . Bosnia, Hamlet is . . . this desk . . . Hamlet is the air, Hamlet is . . . my grandmother, Hamlet is everything you've ever thought about sex, . . . about . . . about . . . geology . . .

JOE. Geology?

TOM (*floundering*). In a very loose sense of course.

JOE. Can you fence?

TOM. I adore to fence . . . I live to fence . . . in a sense I fence to live . . .

> *Cut.*

> *Tom's picture goes up on the board. Underneath, Laertes, Fortinbras, Messengers.*

> *Cut.*

> MAD WOMAN *with two small hand puppets made from paper cups being the Macbeths. She makes weird fanfare noises.*

> MARGARETTA *making cut signs to* JOE.

MAD WOMAN. Have I got it?

JOE. Well, . . . we are going to see a lot of people . . . extraordinary amount of people. I can't say until the end of the cycle . . .

> *Cut.*

> *Close up of a page of* Spotlight *on the desk. Four photographs (all terrible) of the same actor in astonishingly varied disguises. Despite oddly placed facial hair and pipes, he gives the same expression in all four photographs. A look that says 'Hello, I'm barking mad but harmless'. We tilt up to meet, live, the cosy features of* CARNFORTH GREVILLE, *who strangely is giving Joe a look which says 'Hello, I'm barking mad,*

*but harmless'. Older than his years, with an affable calm
that comes only to the terminally eccentric.*

CARNFORTH. . . . amazing isn't it . . . little spirit gum and a little
imagination . . . one becomes totally unrecognisable.

    JOE *in shock.*

CARNFORTH. . . . In my early days in rep they used to call me
Carnforth 'Varied' Greville . . . you know . . . because of all the . . .
you know . . .

JOE. Variety?

CARNFORTH. Yes . . . that's it, variety of characters. Yes.

    Cut.

    CARNFORTH GREVILLE'*s photograph – Rosencrantz,
    Guildenstern, Horatio and Barnardo.*

    Cut.

    TERRY DU BOIS, *a man for whom the word camp was
    invented.*

TERRY. Well, Dorothy Drab's certainly made an impact in here
dahling. I suppose it could be more dreary if you smeared the walls
with sheep's shit, but it's hardly worth it. No, you keep it
anonymous and suicidal darling.

    A gobsmacked look from JOE *who tries to get a word in.*

I'm not playing Polonius darling. Dirty Gerty's got my name on it.
I'm here to play the Queen.

JOE. Now look . . .

TERRY. You haven't had a matronly cleavage near you all week.
You're stuck for mummy and you are looking at the answer to
your prayers. I'm clean, I'm conscientious and I travel with me
own tits.

JOE (*hesitant*). To be perfectly honest with you, I am a bit stuck
and I do want the production to be free and experimental.

TERRY. That's the way I feel about most things darling.

    Cut.

    TERRY'*s photograph takes its place – Gertrude.*

    Cut.

    *Close up on nervous, sweaty person. The man, at the top
    of his voice, begins*

BALDING MAN. Muuule Traaaaaain!!!!

> *And as he launches into the verse, he beats, to the rhythm of the song, an aluminium tray on his head, very hard.*

BALDING MAN. . . . Clippity Cloppin, Clippity Cloppin, down the mountain trail . . .

> *The face of a fervent young Scotsman.*

> *Cut.*

JOE. For me regional accents are not, no problem at all . . . they are vitally important in fact. There is no 'set' voice for Shakespeare . . . that's ridiculous . . .

> *The* GLASWEGIAN *begins to impersonate Olivier's hunchback.*

GLASWEGIAN. I tried this, this morning.

'Noi iz thah wuntre ov r diskantant
Maid glorious summer bai that sun ov York'.

> *It is unintelligible.* JOE *tries to smile.*

> *Cut.*

> *To reveal* VERNON SPATCH. *Blonde, lithe, physique rubbery, personality tough. Cheerful but uncompromising.*

VERNON . . . That's the advantage of being a child actor you see. I've already been in the business for seven centuries.

JOE. It's certainly an impressive C.V.

VERNON. Well, I'm not doing it anymore right? I've got to play someone older. Fourteen years on tour in *Peter Pan* can give you a complex.

> *Cut.*

> VERNON's *picture – Polonius, Marcellus, 1st Gravedigger and Osric.*

> *Cut.*

> *Standing opposite the desk is* NINA RAYMOND, *dark, strange. She stares at* JOE.

JOE. Are your eyes quite alright?

NINA. Perfect.

JOE. It's just that you're not actually looking at me. You're looking just off to one side.

9

NINA. Exactly.

JOE. Oh?

NINA. I often do that when I first meet people. I look off to the side . . . to . . . to watch their aura.

JOE. Their aura?

NINA. Their aura . . . or as often as not just the bit of space next to them which can be very interesting. Can't it?

>   MARGARETTA *gives* JOE *a look, 'What?'*

JOE. Do you wear contact lenses?

NINA. No, . . . they're uncomfortable.

JOE. Well, why don't you wear glasses?

NINA (*aggressive*). I don't need them. (*Beat.*) Can I do my piece now? They said it didn't have to be Shakespeare.

JOE. No.

NINA. Oh good, this is Debbie Harry then.

>   *She begins to sing. Very serious. Tone-deaf and with a*
>   *dance routine that is highly original.*

NINA. 'Once I found love and it was a gas, soon found out had a heart of glass. Seemed like the real thing, only to find what you mistrust, love's gone blind.'

>   *With this she kicks one leg in the air, hits the underside*
>   *of the desk and ends up ass over elbow.*
>
>   *Cut.*
>
>   JOE *is pinning* NINA's *photo to the wall of shame –*
>   *Ophelia, Fortinbras Captain, 2nd Gravedigger,*
>   *Voltimand, Cornelius.*
>
>   *Cut.*

6   INT. AGENT'S OFFICE – END OF DAY.

>   JOE *at the casting board with* MARGARETTA.

JOE. It was always going to be difficult at this time of the year and at such short notice, but we've got a group of people who are really hungry to do it

MARGARETTA. They're hungry because they haven't worked this century.

10

JOE. Neither have I.

Beat.

MARGARETTA. Touché. How am I going to get people in the business down to this God-forsaken venue?

JOE. It's not for those kind of people.

MARGARETTA. What, you mean employer kind of people?

Beat.

JOE. Look, it's a one-off production by a group of (I suspect) mad, but passionate people who are really hungry to do it, who will be performing it in a place that really needs us. If we do it well and honestly everything else will follow.

MARGARETTA. Ooo I love it when you go all visionary. (*Pause.*) Oh, you know you really were close to that movie.

JOE. Oh really?

MARGARETTA. Really. And now Dylan Judd's agent has gone all grand and is asking for millions. Such a mistake.

Beat.

JOE. You'll come won't you?

MARGARETTA. We'll see. I have a feeling it might be worth travelling a very long way for Terry Du Bois's Gertrude.

Cut.

7   EXT. PHONEBOX – DAY.

> MOLLY, JOE*'s sister, in a country phone box. We cut backwards and forwards between her and* JOE, *in the office.*

MOLLY. So when exactly are you going to get to the church?

8   INT. AGENT'S OFFICE – DAY.

JOE. Sunday lunchtime, I hope. Depends on the transport captain.

9   INT. PHONEBOX – DAY.

MOLLY. Why? Who's that?

10   INT. AGENT'S OFFICE – DAY.

JOE. Me.

11   INT. PHONEBOX – DAY.

MOLLY. You're not really going to drive that old heap are you?
With live people in it?

12   INT. AGENT'S OFFICE – DAY.

JOE. Well with actors in it, there is a difference. Anyway I've no
choice. If I'm not paying them any money I've got to look after
them. Look, I'll see you at the top of the hill.

13   INT. PHONEBOX – DAY.

MOLLY. Joe, Joe, What do you mean, top of the hill?

14   INT. AGENT'S OFFICE – DAY.

JOE. By the church gates. Listen, listen, I have to go, I've got get
the food for Sunday. I'm catering manager too. See you love, bye.

15   INT. PHONEBOX – DAY.

MOLLY. No, no Joe, hang on. You don't mean. (*Putting down the
receiver.*) Oh God. (*Exiting the phone-box.*) Oh Christ.

16   EXT. EMPTY CAR PARK – DAY.

> *Sunday Morning. JOE's 'characterful' Volkswagen
> Passat Estate, packed with his new troupe.*
>
> *Camera outside the car, looking from the bonnet through
> the windscreen to the packed car. JOE in the driver's
> seat. HENRY in the passenger's. TERRY in the middle
> of the second row with CARNFORTH and NINA either
> side. TOM and VERNON squeezed like chickens into the
> estate bit.*

NINA V/O. Shall I navigate?

ALLV/O. NO!

JOE V/O. So everybody alright back there?

> *Then in unison with camp actor complicity they drawl
> with languid emphasis.*

ALL V/O. Mahvellous, Daahling.

> *They backfire into the sunset as we*
>
> *Cut.*

17   EXT. COUNTRY LANE – DAY.

> *We hear the in-transit dialogue as the car drives by a
> sign proclaiming their final destination, the village of
> Hope.*

TOM V/O. Oh look, what a beautiful name.

NINA V/O. I think it's a sign.

HENRY V/O. Yes, love, it's a road sign.

TOM V/O. I think it's symbolical.

> *Cut.*

18   EXT. COUNTRY CAR PARK – DAY.

> *They get out of the car.*

JOE. Now look we can't actually get the vehicle any closer than
this. So we'll have to carry the stuff from here. We'll get the rest
later. It is a lovely short walk.

TOM. And up a hill too, how wonderful, perfect after a journey like that.

> *They start to walk up the hill. If* HENRY*'s looks could kill.*

HENRY WAKEFIELD. Wonderful!

> *Cut.*

19   EXT. HILL PATH – DAY.

> *The party make their way up the hill,* TOM *striding ahead of them,* JOE *helping* NINA, *who is walking up the hill on her roller blades.* VERNON *shooting his video,* HENRY *roll-up-ing,* TERRY *mincing,* CARN-FORTH *musing. Various degrees of struggle with bags.*

JOE. We were brought up around here. It was such a beautiful church. Even us kids liked going.

NINA. It's such a shame it's fallen into disuse.

VERNON. Like most of this company.

TERRY. Speak for yourself, you cheeky witch.

HENRY. I must say it's wonderfully accessible for our audience.

CARNFORTH. Ah. 'The road is long, though firm and strong, and tinkly, like a dinner gong.'

HENRY WAKEFIELD. Did you just make that up?

CARNFORTH. No, I think it's by . . . erm . . . no . . . actually . . . I think I did just make it up.

> *Cut.*

20   EXT. PICTURESQUE CHURCH – DAY.

> *They gaze on admiringly.*

VERNON. Actually, that is terrific isn't it? Like out of *Wuthering Heights* or something.

NINA. It's so romantic, and yet so sad.

TERRY. Yes, it's got a sort of feminine sadness, hasn't it Nina? I could make my first entrance from outside.

CARNFORTH. It's certainly worth the trudge isn't it?

TOM. And a fantastic position up here on the hill. There must be some tremendous runs to be had around here.

HENRY WAKEFIELD. It's certainly very atmospheric being surrounded by dead people.

VERNON. Not much of a change from your normal audiences then Harry.

HENRY. Henry.

JOE (*evangelic*). Well, this is it folks, the old hill church of Hope. We're not just doing a play. We're here on a mission. To save this place. To get the developer out and the people back in.

MOLLY V/O. Joe! Joe!

JOE. Ah, this is my sister, Molly.

> MOLLY *approaching breathless from up the hill. She runs into* JOE's *arms – he lifts her up in a hug.*

JOE. How are you?

> *Putting* MOLLY *back down.*

MOLLY. Oh God, you! I thought you'd got it wrong. It's not *this* church. Everybody loves *this* church. It's the big one on the edge of the village.

> *They turn as one to face the village. Beat.*

JOE. Not the big horrible red one?

MOLLY. Yes.

> *Cut.*

21   EXT. UGLY RED CHURCH – DAY.

> *Wide shot. The car now parked outside the big ugly church. The group start to unpack the luggage again.*

HENRY WAKEFIELD. Well, that really is a dog of a church.

VERNON. Graphically, actually it isn't bad, all those nice verticals.

TOM. It's so much flatter round here. Not nearly so good for working the heart rate.

TERRY. Well at least, we can go to town on my dressing room in here love, I do need space for my talent.

VERNON. Space to find it.

TERRY. Shut up.

HENRY. Look, haven't we seen enough? We'll be sick of the sight of the place. Can't we just go to the digs?

JOE. These *are* the digs. It's the only way we can afford to do it.

MOLLY. We've got loads of stuff – food, heaters, sleeping bags, futons.

CARNFORTH. Actually, I'm not terribly keen on Japanese food.

> *Cut.*

22   INT. CHURCH – DAY.

> *Wide shot as the group enter and slowly explore.*

NINA. Gosh, it's incredibly atmospheric.

VERNON. And damp.

JOE. I remember this place. We used to get dragged in here once a month on a Sunday night for 'extra' religion.

MOLLY. Oh yes, Mum and Dad made sure we got our money's worth alright.

CARNFORTH. And have you kept it up?

TERRY. Carnforth, watch your language.

TOM. He means the faith, have you kept up the faith.

> *They walk down the nave together.*

No, it's terribly hard. I mean, I'm tremendously spiritual, but it's still very difficult for me to meditate for more than an hour each day.

HENRY WAKEFIELD. Yes, I expect that's about all Buddha can take from you isn't it?

NINA. So Molly, why doesn't anyone use this place anymore?

MOLLY. Well they do, or rather they did until this bloody developer got hold of it. I mean basically a lot of people have abandoned Hope.

HENRY. I know how they feel love.

> *In walks, very slowly,* FADGE. *She is clearly communing with something other worldly. Cloths in hair and an ensemble of bizarre bits, she reduces the others to awed silence. She moves as if re-enacting Grasshopper's walk across the rice paper in* Kung Fu.

TOM. Ooo what dramas! Is this the landlord?

JOE. Oh, right, right. Let me introduce you. Our designer. This is Fadge.

NINA. Did he say Vadge?

TOM. I'm glad she uses the abbreviation.

FADGE (*she stops*). FADGE darling, Fuh, Fuh, Fuh, give it an F.

TERRY. I think it's a bit early in the day for that darling.

TOM. Is this entire production going to be conducted through a stream of innuendo?

NINA. Is there a surname Fadge?

VERNON. Yes, is it Fadge Smith? or Fadge Fadginton? or . . .

FADGE. Just Fadge darling. (*She stops.*) You know this place is incredible. I feel something very powerful here. Very strange and powerful.

NINA. Powerful and strange, I feel that too Fadge.

VERNON. Powerful and strange and damp.

JOE. I was just saying Fadge, there's some marvellous opportunities here for –

FADGE. You see, we must make the design all about Space. People in space, things in space, women in space, men in space.

TOM. So we'd be sort of . . . spacemen?

FADGE (*panicked*). In a sense.

> *Cut.*

23   INT. CRYPT – DAY.

> *Campbeds, heaters, a rough dorm.*

VERNON. So Carnforth, we get to sleep in the crypt. Do you think they might be trying to imply something about our acting?

CARNFORTH. What, that it's a bit cryptic?

VERNON. No, that it's dead.

CARNFORTH. I don't know, I've seen worse in the army.

VERNON. Were you in the army?

CARNFORTH (*thinks*). Um . . . No, not strictly speaking, no, but plays about the army, certainly. (*Then rather nervously.*) Vernon, do you think the boss would be offended if I popped out to recce the local hostelry, in lieu of this evening meal?

VERNON. I don't know Carnforth. Why don't you ask him?

> *He leaves.*

> *Cut.*

24   INT. KITCHEN – DAY.

> TERRY *and* MOLLY *unpacking food.*

TERRY. We're talking about actors, darling, not civilians. Discipline is what they need.

MOLLY. But you're not here for long. Really, it'll sort itself out.

TERRY. Twenty-one days love, sixty-three meals and eight trillion cups of tea. I don't know how many ass-wipes that runs to, but you don't want to be the one holding the loo roll, you'll take my advice. We'll draw up the cleaning and cooking rota *now*.

MOLLY. It's so long since I've spent time with Joe. I'd forgotten how actors behave. This is just like being in the Boy Scouts.

TERRY. Don't say that love. My pants will never dry.

> *Cut.*

25   INT. CHURCH – DAY.

> HENRY, *agitated, striding through the chapel,* JOE *trying to keep up with him.*

HENRY. I don't see why I have to share with the pouffe, love.

JOE. Oh, come on now Harry.

HENRY. Henry.

JOE. We're people of the world. A person's sexuality is irrelevant.

HENRY. I couldn't care less if he shags hamsters or not. They're all the same. The entire British Theatre's dominated by the class system and a bunch of Oxbridge Homos.

JOE. I don't think Terry's Oxbridge.

HENRY. Well, it hardly matters, they're all drama Queens. I hope your Gertrude's a quiet woman.

JOE (*stricken*). Yes, . . . I wanted to have a word with you about that actually . . .

HENRY. When does she arrive, by the way? I hope she's not going to be late for the read-through.

> *They walk up to what will clearly be the 'stage'.*

JOE. We should probably find five minutes before then, just to explain my concept of your Queen.

HENRY. It's not bad though is it? The stage feels good, you can command the audience. Henry Irving would have loved this . . .

> *The smell of Dr. Footlights has suddenly transported Henry. His posture changes. He looks out, eyes alight into some imaginary, darkened auditorium. He begins to speak, normally at first and then as he quotes, he moves into a barely intelligible rendition of Henry Irving.*

'Eet eez the cahz, eet eez the cahz, may sool, let me naht name it to you, you chaysd stahz, eet eez the cahz'.

> *He breaks out of the spell.*

Irving as he would have played Othello, love. Very strange gestures, but totally hypnotic.

> *Beat.*

JOE. Look are you going to be OK with the bedroom arrangements? We could ask somebody to move.

HENRY. Alright, alright, I'll stay there. I can always sleep with me ass in a bucket.

> *Cut.*

26 INT. UPSTAIRS GALLERY (GIRLS' BEDROOM) – DAY.

NINA *unpacking*. FADGE *sketching*.

NINA. Oh, *Hamlet* at Christmas! With a group of like-minded artists in a rough but thrillingly real location. I can't think of anything that would make this job better.

FADGE. A salary?

> NINA *tries to look at* FADGE's *drawings and model.*

NINA. Is that the design for the . . . ?

> FADGE *quickly hugs the design to her.*

FADGE. It's not finished yet.

NINA. Sorry.

> NINA *goes to her bag.*

NINA. Where did I put my moisturizer?

> *Beat.*

FADGE. You can call me 'Fuh'.

NINA. What?

FADGE. It's a nickname. Really close friends call me 'Fuh'.

NINA (*slowly*). Oh, well I'm very touched that you should allow me to use it . . . I mean it's slightly harder to say than Fadge but it's beautiful . . . 'Fuh' . . . thank you.

> NINA *has found her cream and starts to apply it liberally to her face.*

FADGE. Why are you rubbing low calorie mayonnaise into your face?

> *Cut.*

27   INT. CHURCH – NIGHT.

> *Wide shot. Trestle table. Everyone gathered round. Chilli consumed. Red wine being enjoyed.*

VERNON. Here's to Molly, Cheers!

> *A chorus of 'Well done, Molly' etc.*

CARNFORTH. That's rather an acceptable little Chianti.

HENRY. Well, you've certainly given it a good road test, haven't you? You carry on drinking like this, it'll affect next year's harvest.

JOE. Actually, it is just worth talking a little about the food and drink situation.

> *We start to track along the table.*

VERNON. Yes, when do we get our expenses, love?

JOE. Well, the point is I suppose that the most economic way of doing this is to operate our household budget from a central fund.

VERNON. You mean there are no expenses?

JOE. Not in the conventional sense.

VERNON. Is there another sense?

HENRY. Well there's the crooked-bastard-who-didn't-tell-us-before-we-got-the-job sense.

NINA. Now that's not fair. You wanted this job. This is Joe's own money. He must spend it how he thinks fit.

TERRY. Here, here.

NINA. This was a very generous meal.

TOM. Yes, the chilli was very nice but it really has to be the last red meat I have. I mean already I'm going to have to detox and irrigate. Colonically this has set me right back.

JOE. Yes, sorry Tom, we'll all bear that in mind as we implement the cooking roster. Now Molly, thank God is going to do the shopping for supplies, but we probably will need to be economic with our provisions.

HENRY. I think she means you've drunk our entire Christmas wine allowance Mr Greville.

CARNFORTH. I hope not.

TERRY (*to* HENRY). Oh, leave her alone, Mrs Grumpy. I think Nancy Nerves is rattling your bars about tomorrow isn't she?

NINA. Yes, I'm nervous too. My stomach's full of snakes. You know, some people get butterflies in their tummy, I get sort of snake things.

VERNON. Those are your intestines love.

> *The camera has come to stop with* FADGE *in the foreground in a trance*

FADGE. I can feel my nipples stiffening.

> *All heads turn to look.*

FADGE. It's a good sign. A very good sign.

More silence.

Hard and quick. Hard and quick. If it happens the night before a production – I feel it to be a tremendous omen.

More silence.

TERRY. Well, we've never short of a shock from Mr Mad are we?

MOLLY. Excuse me, what is all this? Calling boys by girls' names? I'm completely lost.

TERRY. Camp, darling. Theatrical camp. Banter. Keeps us all on the straight and narrow. Put a girl's name in front of any word, just to spice up your sentences. And always refer to a man as a *she* and a woman as a *he*. For example if I were to comment on Harry over there.

HENRY. Henry.

TERRY. I might say, 'Oo Mandy Misery's shafted Mrs Wakefield good and proper hasn't she?'

MOLLY. I see.

TERRY. Well you will darling. You never know, there might be a little more campery before the first night.

They all react to that.

28   INT. KITCHEN – NIGHT.

TOM, MOLLY, NINA, FADGE *and* JOE. *Washing and clearing away.*

MOLLY. The point is there is nowhere for people to go, apart from the pub. If they can afford it. I mean, there's no village hall, there's no arts centre. I mean, we need this place to give people a focus. Prove to the council that there is a community worth maintaining. That there *is* a community.

NINA. Oh, then it would be wonderful if it was a great production.

TOM. Don't feel under any pressure Joe.

MOLLY. What is the show anyway? That bugger wouldn't even tell me. I hope it's something Christmassy, a comedy.

Beat.

TOM. It's *Hamlet.*

Beat.

22

MOLLY. Great. Hello kids. Do stop watching *Mighty Morphin Power Rangers* and come and watch a four hundred year-old play about a depressed aristocrat. I mean it's something you can really relate to.

JOE. We've got our work cut out.

MOLLY. Who's playing Hamlet?

> *Beat.*

Oh no. That's bloody typical of you. It's so bloody boring.

> JOE *picks* MOLLY *up and carries her out of the kitchen.*

JOE. Come on Molly, I'll take you home. You can walk off your disappointment.

> NINA *runs off after them.*

NINA. Can I come too? Just for the air.

> *Cut.*

29   EXT. PICTURESQUE HILLSIDE CHURCH – NIGHT.

> NINA *and* JOE *returning from* MOLLY*'s. A romantic silhouette of the building.* JOE *in remote reflective mood.* NINA, *a good listener.*

JOE. I hope you didn't mind coming this route. It's on our way home.

NINA. Not at all. It's a chance to calm down after all the excitement. I couldn't have got to sleep right away.

JOE. I just wanted to see this place again, you know. I'd set my heart on it.

NINA. The other church is much more practical.

JOE. I know, but this is where I grew up. It's just typically stupid of me not to have checked properly with Moll. Charging away as usual.

NINA. That's enthusiasm. It's important. Not many people have it like you.

JOE. I hope I can keep it up.

NINA. I beg your pardon!

JOE. Don't you start.

Beat.

NINA. Are you scared about tomorrow?

JOE. Absolutely petrified. Right now I wish I'd got that stupid part in that stupid film and just had to turn up for six months in a funny suit and drink tea all day.

NINA. Look, we're all right behind you. You won't fail.

JOE. I did once before, you know. Fadge and I both. Different shows. Same bull at a gate mentality. Complete cock-up. All money lost, all confidence lost with it. The day it went bust my fiancée left me for another man. Wonderful timing. Only an actress can carry that off. No offence. I shouldn't be talking to you like this, should I?

NINA. I'm flattered that you can confide in me. Martin always says that if you can face your troubles and fears and just acknowledge them, then you're halfway to letting them fly away. I always try to remember that.

JOE. That's good advice. Who's Martin?

NINA. My husband.

Cut.

Caption, white on black

ACT II

'THERE'S NO BUSINESS LIKE SHOWBUSINESS!'

30 INT. CHURCH – DAY.

> *Wide shot of the group gathered around a trestle table for the read-through. FADGE is sitting on the stage overlooking the cast and sketching.*

JOE. Right! This is obviously a very exciting moment. We're about to embark on this voyage of discovery. I'd like talk a little about *Hamlet*.

Now I see it as a very *dark* play –

TOM. I see it as a very *long* play, darling. Sally Scissors is going to appear we hope?

JOE. Yes, yes. I've got a lot of cuts, but what I'd like to do for the benefit of this read-through is to read the whole thing.

HENRY. Oh great, we're only got ten days to rehearse but let's spend fifteen hours reading the whole bloody thing on day one.

JOE. I'll give you the cuts directly afterwards.

NINA. It's vital that we read the whole thing once.

CARNFORTH *and* TOM. Here, here.

JOE (*hyper-tense*). Right, right, rather than waste any more time, you know on speeches and things, I would like to say at this stage, please enjoy the reading. I mean, don't feel obliged to give, you know, performances. I don't want that, but do avoid mumbling and just throwing it away – let's really hear the play. Let's really listen to each other. And *relax*. OK. Off we go –

> *Various members of the cast start to light cigarettes.*

TOM. Can I just mention smoking. I think it would be a really good idea. If this was a non-smoking read-through.

> *The atmosphere could be cut with a knife.*

JOE. Right, right, No, if we could all be sensitive to that. Thanks very much Tom. OK. OK.

> *Cut.*

31   INT. CHURCH – DAY.

CARNFORTH. 'Who's there?'

TERRY (*as Gertrude*). 'Good Hamlet, cast thy nighted colour off, And let thine eye look like a friend on Denmark.'

> HENRY *in shock. Yes, Gertrude will be played by a man.*

TERRY. 'Do not for ever with thy vailed lids
Seek for thy noble father in the dust'.

> HENRY *fuming, starts to roll-up a cigarette. We cut as Noël Coward treats us to another chorus of biting wit to accompany our*

32   READ-THROUGH MONTAGE:

> *Noël Coward lyrics, part II. Montage close-ups of nervous hands, fiddling with sweet packets, lighters,*

> *matches and cigarettes. Tapping feet. Script pages turning. One by one the cast begins to smoke.* TOM *tries to avoid it.* MOLLY *hides a yawn.* FADGE *tweaks her nipples.*

> *We end on a close-up of the last page of the play, then to a wide-shot of the entire company engulfed in cigarette smoke. The cast leave the table coughing.*

33   EXT. CHURCHYARD – DAY.

> *The side doors of the church open and out pour the company for a coffee break. They are led by an irate* HENRY *followed by a grovelling* JOE.

HENRY. I can't stand pouffes!

JOE. Henry –

HENRY. Gertrude was not written as a shirtlifter.

JOE. Shakespeare himself was probably bisexual.

HENRY. Bollocks!

JOE. It's an Elizabethan concept, it'll free up a whole part of the show.

HENRY. A dyke I could have coped with, I don't mind the odd diesel, but I'm not having me tongue down that.

> *They stomp away out of shot, but the galloping duo continue to dance in and out of the back of the frame as the rest of the scene goes on. The rest of the cast perch for a coffee.*

TERRY. Methinks the lady doth protest too much, dahling.

VERNON. He's old school, love. He's just trying to prove that he's really twenty-nine, with six testicles and a four-foot dick.

CARNFORTH (*tentatively*). Look chaps, I'm just nipping down to the . . . post office for a quick . . . stamp.

TOM. I cannot believe the cuts, I cannot believe the cuts, I cannot believe the cuts.

VERNON. Can you believe the cuts Tom?

TOM. No, I can't believe them.

NINA. Tom, you're playing all those parts. I mean, that's the real challenge isn't it? To make them all exciting and different.

VERNON. And brief.

TOM. Exactly. I'm going to speak to my agent.

TERRY. That's right, darling, threaten to walk. The management will quake in their boots.

NINA. Oh please don't leave, Tom. I think you'd be a wonderful Laertes.

TOM. Well I have put quite a lot of work into it actually. Normally I'd have tried to spend a month in Denmark to get it right.

VERNON. So what did you do this time?

TOM. Well, I borrowed this book on the Eiffel Tower . . . You know in the play he goes to France? I just wanted an image in my head.

TERRY. Well there's plenty of room for it, darling.

> *The noise of* HENRY *and* JOE *arguing is still at fever pitch.*

MOLLY. Is Joe alright?

TERRY. Oh, he's fine love, he's just humouring Mrs Wakefield.

MOLLY. Will he leave? Is it always like this on the first day of a play?

NINA. It's sort of political I think.

VERNON. Marking out territory.

TERRY. Yes, she's a ruthless step-daughter that one.

MOLLY. Did you enjoy the read-through Fadge?

FADGE. I thought it was extraordinary. And also, in a strange way banal.

VERNON. Does that mean you've decided on an extraordinarily banal design.

FADGE. I can't – I never decide at this stage. One has to remain open.

VERNON. Open and indecisive?

FADGE. No, – I –

NINA. Oh, stop teasing, Vernon. I can't wait to see the set model . . . Fuh.

VERNON (*to Terry*). Fur?

TERRY. Did she say Fur?

> *Cut.*

27

34   INT. CHURCH – DAY.

*Close-up on the Set Model being revealed from under a
box by* FADGE. *It is a cardboard replica of the church's
interior. The cast stare silently.* NINA's *face in very
close to it.* HENRY, *placated, is nevertheless in a roll-
up-sulk. Long pause.*

CARNFORTH. Um . . . Isn't this . . . um . . . (*He burps.*) pardon.

TERRY. You'll have to go easy licking those stamps at lunchtime
Mrs Greville.

CARNFORTH. Yes, but . . . this is sort of exactly . . . where we
are . . . isn't it?

FADGE. Exactly.

TOM. Brilliant.

VERNON. So what's the design?

FADGE. Smoke.

NINA. Smoke?

FADGE. People in space, in smoke.

HENRY. Oh Christ.

FADGE. This building does everything else. Smoke gives us
atmosphere, mystery.

VERNON. Bronchitis.

TERRY. What about period then, darling?

FADGE. Joe . . . ?

JOE. Well, I think we should create the period. I mean I don't
think it should be Elizabethan, that would be ridiculous.

TOM. Although, it is an Elizabethan play isn't it?

HENRY. Oh, don't bring up the tedious details love.

JOE. It should be no period, it should be our period. When
everyone's come up with contributions for character and costume,
the period and style will emerge. That's the nature of this
collaboration.

VERNON. Is 'cop-out' one word or two?

NINA. I think you're being a naughty cynical sausage there,
Vernon.

Major camp 'shock' reaction from everyone.

28

JOE. Yes, thank you Nina. We'll be having those discussions this afternoon about character and costume to set us all off on the right foot. We'll start rehearsals properly tomorrow with the first scene of the play.

TERRY. Starting with the first scene? Oo she's so radical.

JOE. Shut up bitch.

>*Cut.*

35   EXT. FADGE'S VAN – AFTERNOON.

>FADGE *pulling out costumes, lights and props from the back of her van. Talking to herself.*

FADGE. Bring everything with me. That's what Joe said. And the style will emerge. Hopefully.

>*Cut.*

36   INT. CHURCH – AFTERNOON.

>*A montage of the afternoon's work. The camera remains in one position throughout. We jump cut. Manic activity in the back of all these scenes.* TERRY *is with a nervous* FADGE *at the costume rail.*

TERRY. I wear me own frocks love. I bring me own breasts. You look after the other children.

>*Cut.*

>JOE *and* CARNFORTH *talking.*

CARNFORTH. Yes, the thing is Joe, I noticed that I'm actually playing two characters that appear on stage at the same time, as it were . . . ?

>*Cut.*

>JOE *and* TOM.

TOM. Actually Joe, I just wondered if I could mention the cuts. I think they are brilliant, brilliant, so clever what you have done. It's just that Laertes has lost four key lines.

>*Cut.*

Back to JOE *and* CARNFORTH.

CARNFORTH. Perhaps you maybe planned something, perhaps with mirrors?

> *Cut.*

> *Back to* TOM *and* JOE.

TOM. Just wondered if at some point you might consider reinstating them.

JOE. Well, no,

TOM. No, let me do it for you –

'Oh Hamlet!'

> *Cut.*

> HENRY *with his trousers off being measured by* FADGE.

HENRY. Are you going to be much longer? It's freezing in here.

> *Cut.*

> JOE *and* CARNFORTH.

JOE. It's more a movement thing that I envisaged.

CARNFORTH. Movement? . . . ah . . .

JOE. Fadge will help you.

> *Cut.*

> *Back to* JOE *and* TOM. *The latter finishing his excerpt with a flourish.*

TOM. Do you see what I mean?

> *Cut.*

> HENRY *with trousers off, having his inside leg measured.*

HENRY. Careful, Careful.

> *Cut.*

> VERNON *crosses frame with his video camera.*

> *Cut.*

> HENRY *crosses frames in the opposite direction.*

HENRY. Can't we get the frocks sorted out!

> *Cut.*

JOE *and* TOM.

TOM. And then I think he could rip his shirt off and abseil down from the organ for 'where is my father'. They do some wonderful body oils now.

    Cut.

    NINA *and* FADGE *race through shot.*

NINA. I don't want her to wear glasses.

FADGE. You practically fell over the balcony getting into bed last night.

    TOM *rubbing oil into his bare chest.*

TOM. Doesn't the light read on this?

    Cut.

    JOE *talking to* VERNON.

VERNON. I think a big nose would be great . . . Did you see *Cyrano de Bergerac* . . . ? That kind of size.

    Cut.

HENRY. I want huge shoulder pads. He's got to be butch.

    Cut.

37   INT. JOE'S OFFICE – NIGHT.

    JOE *and* MOLLY *working at opposite ends of a trestle table in front of the altar* – JOE'*s makeshift office.*

JOE. Now, look you're actually going to have to be me during these rehearsals, so I can watch the scenes.

MOLLY. Oh great. Thanks for the warning. So unlike you. So how does Herr Direktor rehearse his part?

JOE. We'll find time. And I'll nick all your best bits. I seem to remember that you were rather better than me during all those amateur dramatics.

MOLLY. Well yes, 'cos that's where I do it, as opposed to thinking someone might pay me to do it.

JOE. Yes, it's a horrible concept that, isn't it? It's caught me out before now.

MOLLY. But you still persist.

JOE. Just about. I think this is what we call the last gasp.

MOLLY. So why don't you make it easier on yourself this time by doing a comedy, or something somebody might be interested to see?

JOE. Well, that's where you and me part company as always. I think if we can do it with humour, passion and reality people *will* be interested in seeing it. I saw this play when I was fifteen, and it changed my life. You don't forget that. I don't think I was any different then to any of your hormonally confused kids now. All I was ever interested in was girls and wanking. Unfortunately, hardly ever in that order. I saw this play and it spoke to my heart, and my head, and my chief reproductive organ.

MOLLY. Can that go in the programme notes?

>JOE *throws a ball of paper at* MOLLY.
>
>*Cut.*

38   INT. CHURCH – MORNING.

>FADGE *is taking a warm-up session with the cast.*
>*A bizarre collection of trussed up, semi-lycraed wrecks.*
>FADGE *beats a drum and makes noises. The others*
>*sway, bend and stretch with varying degrees of commit-*
>*ment. It's like a scene from* One Flew Over the Cuckoo's
>Nest.

FADGE. Release that pain, get it out, throw it away, up and down, up and down, out of your head . . . and now it becomes a . . . train of fear . . . a train of fear . . . and vocalise . . . poop poop . . . poop poop . . .

>*Cut.*

39   INT. CHURCH STAGE – DAY.

>CARNFORTH *is giving us his Bernardo.*
>*Unconvincingly.*

CARNFORTH. 'Who's there?'

>VERNON *as Francisco is about to carry on.* JOE *leaps*
>*up on the stage. The rest of the company are sitting in the*
>*auditorium.*

JOE. Great. Terrific. Huge potential there.

> JOE *moves* CARNFORTH *to one side.* CARNFORTH *crashes his pike into the scenery.*

CARNFORTH. Sorry. Sorry.

JOE. It's a bit limp.

CARNFORTH. Limp?

JOE. Well you know. He has seen a ghost and he is probably expecting to see another one. Listen, *Hamlet* is a tremendous ghost story. I want to see that fear – I want to smell that fear.

CARNFORTH. Oh, I see. I see. That's good. Fear.

JOE. Alright. Start again.

> JOE *goes back to his seat.*

CARNFORTH. 'Who's there?'

> *No difference.*

JOE (*running up to* CARNFORTH). No. No. No. It still doesn't convince me. Now look let's take a little time out here to ground this in some sort of reality. You tell me, Carnforth, when was the last time you were really terrified. Can you remember when that was or if there was such a time?

CARNFORTH. Um . . . yes . . . Yes I can remember, I was on my way to have Sunday lunch with my Mum. It was her birthday I remember . . . bit of a 'do' . . . you know. And I got a flat tyre on the motorway and well it was touch and go whether I would get there on time and I was . . . pretty terrified then . . . you know . . .

JOE. And how did this terror manifest itself?

CARNFORTH. Well . . . it probably took a little longer to change the tyre than it would have . . . hands shaking, that sort of thing.

JOE. Right. Look let's bring that situation here. That fear. (*Leaving the stage.*) Alright, let's have another go.

> JOE *runs back to the auditorium.* CARNFORTH *starts again. This time miming changing a tyre.*

CARNFORTH. 'Who's there?'

JOE. No. No. No. You don't have to change the tyre.

CARNFORTH. I'm so sorry. Sorry everybody. I thought you wanted . . .

> *Cut.*

40 EXT. CHURCHYARD – DAY.

> TOM *massaging* FADGE's *hand strenuously.* NINA *sits with them munching on some celery.*

TOM. Tricky first morning.

NINA. Yes, first scenes, they're always so difficult.

TOM. I can feel the production in here already . . . I can feel your pain.

FADGE. Can you Tom?

TOM. Relax.

> TOM *gives one final agonising squeeze.* FADGE *shrieks.*
>
> *Cut.*

41 INT. STAGE – DAY.

> *The first court scene. It has been going well.* HENRY *in full voice, very pleased with himself.* TERRY *in practice skirt and falsies.*

HENRY. ' . . . But now my cousin Hamlet and my son'

MOLLY. 'A little more than kin and less than kind'

HENRY. 'How is it that the clouds still hang on you?'

MOLLY. 'Not so my lord, I am too much i' the sun'

> TERRY *begins in a put-on voice of throaty, grande-dame theatricality.*

TERRY. 'Good Hamlet, cast thy nighted colour off
And let thine eye look like a friend on Denmark.'

> HENRY *stops.*

HENRY. Is he going to do it like that?

TERRY. Like what, you rude girl?

HENRY. Like Larry the Lamb on speed.

JOE. Right, now let me just stop you both there. Henry, if you could leave the interruptions to me. Thank you. Terry, look I am slightly concerned about the voice. The general movement fine but the voice is just a little . . .

34

TERRY. But it's what they all do darling. All the *grande dames*. They don't talk like they do in the real world. They put on the old cigarette gravel. The tragic trill. The emotional break in the middle of the line, the operatic cadenzas, . . . I'm not making it up, they do.

JOE. Sure and sometimes it's very good, and sometimes they're very wrong and give Shakespeare a bad name. Technically it's brilliant . . . but you don't sound like a . . . human being.

HENRY. More like a robot with piles.

JOE. That's not what I meant.

TERRY. Look that's what I hear love when I go to the classical theatre. I thought that's what you did.

JOE. Have a little think about something more natural. I think you'd do it brilliantly. (*Leaving the stage.*) Alright, here we go.

> *Beat.*

NINA. Actually, Terry, something to be aware of. Somebody told me about it. You must be very careful that you don't invert your opening line as Gertrude. Apparently it's quite a famous cock-up so that instead of saying 'Good Hamlet, cast thy nighted colour off' you can end up saying ' Good Hamlet cast off thy coloured nightie'.

> *Embarrassed pause.*

You probably won't do that yourself . . . I just . . . anyone like some tea?

> *Cut.*

42   INT. JOE'S OFFICE – NIGHT.

> JOE *in his make-shift office, sorting out papers.* MOLLY *arrives in full rage carrying a letter.*

MOLLY. Bloody Landlord!

JOE. What?

MOLLY. Well you know you paid the rent?

JOE. Yeah, three weeks in advance.

MOLLY. Well, he says he wants a week's rent out of that for unpaid electric bills that he says the school's liable for.

35

JOE. Are you liable?

MOLLY. Of course not. He's chancing his arm.

JOE. Well, challenge it.

MOLLY. We will, but he's stalling, till after Christmas.

JOE. Oh, can he do that?

MOLLY. Of course not. But he's a shit and he already has your cash.

JOE. What does that mean?

MOLLY. Well, that as far as he's concerned he wants another week's rent or he'll turf us out.

JOE. Well we won't go.

MOLLY. Well if we do that he says he'll cut off all the services, water, gas, electric.

JOE. Bloody hell, Moll.

MOLLY. I've spoken to the council. He's within his rights. If us or the school doesn't pay up, we contravene the terms of the special performing licence.

JOE. Oh come on, we don't have time for that.

MOLLY. I didn't plan it, Joe.

JOE. When's his deadline?

MOLLY. End of the final week. Day before we open.

JOE. Or?

MOLLY. He'll send his mates in to close us down.

JOE. Christ, I don't have £700.

MOLLY. Well neither do I.

JOE. Alright, alright. We'll think of something. Don't tell the actors.

> NINA *comes into the office. She has her coat on. They switch into cheery mode.*

NINA. Sorry to interrupt. Just came to say well done. Both of you. Wonderful first day. You were so brave. It's all very exciting.

JOE. Thanks very much Nina.

MOLLY. Are you off out for the evening?

NINA. Oh no. It's Tom's turn to cook. We're having vegetarian steak and kidney pudding. I wouldn't miss that for the world. I'm just off to the phone box. See you later.

MOLLY. Who's she off to ring?

JOE. Her husband.

>   *Cut.*

43   INT. CHURCH NOTICE BOARD – NIGHT.

>   JOE *is pinning the rehearsal call to the board.* VERNON
>   *is putting something up on the wall.*

VERNON. Well boss, another day, another .00001 of a dollar. How was it for you?

JOE. Not without its moments Vernon.

>   VERNON *reveals what he was hanging, a poster –*
>   *Vernon's name in massive type –* VERNON SPATCH IS
>   POLONIUS IN . . .

VERNON. Not bad eh? Just a bit of fun.

JOE. No, no, it works well. A little understated I fear.

VERNON. Well, it's worth it just to see Henry's face. By the way boss, are you considering having anyone come to see this thing?

JOE. First things first Vernon. We've got to get the show right.

VERNON. But what about tickets, box-office, the cash-advance, advertising?

JOE. That's all in hand. You know, they set up a box-office at Molly's school and people can book through her home number. Fadge has agreed to do the catering and the front of house etc. So we're geared up.

VERNON. And how many people are currently booked?

JOE. Well, you know figures can be a bit misleading at this time of the year, Christmas shopping etc.

VERNON. Has anyone booked?

JOE. We're looking at business mainly on the night.

VERNON. No one's booked?

JOE. Not yet. No.

>   *Cut.*

44   EXT. PHONE BOX – NIGHT.

> *We cut between* JOE *and* MARGARETTA *on the telephone. She is at home, in bed, reading a script.*

JOE. I've got a bit of a cash flow problem with the landlord.

MARGARETTA. Oh Joe, not again, you promised.

JOE. Yeah, I'm just a bit stuck.

MARGARETTA. Well unstick yourself darling. I'm sure you can reason with him.

JOE. I don't think so. He's got some strong and very persuasive friends in the building trade.

MARGARETTA. You'll think of something. And how's your Hamlet?

JOE. Well a little underdone at the moment. Molly's mainly filling in for me, but she's rather good too the bitch.

MARGARETTA. Don't undervalue yourself darling. I don't want to drag reluctant casting directors down there to see you being bad.

JOE. No. Understood.

MARGARETTA. Oh and darling, more dramas on the Dylan Judd front. Apparently she wants billing and a personal trainer. Contacts not signed, filming imminent. Oooh she's pushing her luck.

JOE. I do wish him well.

MARGARETTA. I'll keep you posted. Are you feeling less suicidal now?

JOE. I suppose so.

MARGARETTA. Then it's working. Marvellous. Good night sweet prince.

JOE. Goodnight.

> *Cut.*

45   INT. CHURCH STAGE – DAY.

> *Rehearsals in progress.* TOM, VERNON *and* NINA. *The others dotted around.* VERNON *is being very theatrical.* TOM *is using an accent from another solar system.* JOE *watches aghast.*

VERNON. ' . . . and let him ply his music'

TOM. 'Well my lord'

VERNON. 'Farewell'

JOE (*to* VERNON). Hold on a sec. Um . . . it's a bit . . .

VERNON. Much?

JOE. Yes . . . I don't know if the nose is going to your head, if you'll pardon the expression, but I'm getting more Shylock than Polonius.

VERNON. I like to be bold early on but I get the message chief. It's basically L.C.A.

JOE. Um?

VERNON. Less Crap Acting.

JOE. That's about the size of it. Thank you. Tom?

TOM. Yes, darling.

JOE. Your accent.

TOM. Oh you noticed it.

JOE. I think you'd have to be from Pluto not to notice it.

TOM. Good, good.

JOE. Unfortunately, I think you also have to come from Pluto to understand it.

TOM (*bridling*). It has to be different darling. I am playing lots of roles, however small some of them are now. I want each one to be distinct. I've taken my cue from his name: Reynaldo – you know, Reynard – sort of foxy you know, hence the accent.

JOE. A foxy accent?

TOM. Well, you see, I asked myself how would a fox speak? Rather covert, rather secretive.

JOE. I'm getting more Russian than secretive or foxy.

TOM. Let me work on it.

JOE. Alright, thank you. OK, here we go then.

NINA. Joe, before we do my entrance, I wondered if I could try something?

JOE. Yes, certainly Nina.

NINA. I was thinking, bearing in mind what you were saying to Carnforth the other day. You know, about fear and everything and I was sort of thinking for this scene that she really ought to be genuinely scared to bits.

JOE. Exactly.

NINA. I mean, almost violent, hysterical, just preparing the audience slightly for later on when she goes mad, and so that we can really see the effect Hamlet has on her. The effect of seeing his flesh, the sexual threat, you know, just very much 'out of control' almost . . .

JOE. Excellent. Right. You try it.

Listen, in your own time.

> *They begin the scene again.* VERNON *is more natural.* TOM *is less Russian.*

VERNON. 'Goodbye ye, fare ye well.'

TOM. 'Good my lord'

VERNON. 'And let him ply his music'

TOM. 'Well, my lord'

VERNON. 'Farewell'

> *At this point with a great scream* NINA *rushes from the back of the church. She is possessed by the role. She is also blind.*

NINA. 'Oh my lord I have been so affrighted.'

> VERNON *holds open his arms. She runs past him, off the edge of the steps, and lands, everything akimbo, face down on the floor with a great thud.*

46   INT. CHURCH – DAY.

> *In the background* JOE *and* TOM *are performing primitive first aid on* NINA, *while* VERNON *films. In foreground* FADGE *is sewing a costume,* CARNFORTH *is filling in his crossword.*

FADGE. If that girl makes it to the first night without serious accident, I'll be amazed.

CARNFORTH. I know, she does seem to have a bit of a vision problem doesn't she.

40

FADGE. She's brushed her teeth with soap for the last three nights. But she won't admit it.

CARNFORTH. Yes, she's a stubborn old thing under all that dizzy stuff.

FADGE. But nice, very nice.

> FADGE *starts to pull apart the costume she's sewing.*

FADGE. Oh buggering, buggery, bugger.

CARNFORTH. You alright?

FADGE. No . . . it's these bloody costumes – I've brought every period with me but I can't quite decide and it's getting a bit . . .

CARNFORTH. Late in the day?

FADGE. Don't say that for God's sake. (*Beat.*) You're very impressive with that crossword.

CARNFORTH. Well, you know what the secret is? I don't answer any of the clues.

FADGE. What do you mean?

CARNFORTH. I just take my time and fill in all the empty boxes. Any old letters will do. I've always been terrible at the bloody things. But it takes my mind off the God awful business of acting.

FADGE. Is your name really Carnforth Greville?

CARNFORTH. No, it's Keith Branch. I just pinched one that I thought had the requisite amount of mystery and glamour.

FADGE. What did your parents think?

CARNFORTH. They were rather disappointed actually. Well, they'd done a lot of scrimping to put me through drama school and whatnot. Well, they really believed in me. Mum especially. I don't think I've dealt with parental expectation terribly well. What about you? Were you christened Fadge?

FADGE. Hardly. I was christened Mildred. Not the name to have if you seek distinction as a designer which I rather pitifully did. But I was adopted you see, so I didn't think it really mattered.

CARNFORTH. I think it's rather sweet.

FADGE. Thank you Keith.

CARNFORTH. My pleasure, Mildred.

> FADGE *looks around the church.*

FADGE. It's rather fun all this sometimes isn't it?

CARNFORTH. It is rather. Ooo, I've just got another clue.

> *Cut.*

47   EXT. PICTURESQUE CHURCH BENCH – DAY.

> NINA *sits with sandwich in hand and bandage on head, disconsolate.* JOE *offers her some tea from his vacuum flask.*

JOE. So why, no glasses ah? Or . . . I don't know . . .

NINA. I don't know either. I don't want to see the world in sharp focus.

JOE. Why?

NINA. Because it's horrible.

JOE. Do you really think so? You're always so amazingly positive and bright.

NINA. And dizzy?

JOE. No, I didn't say that.

NINA. That's what Dad says on the phone every night. He thinks this whole thing of being an actress and working in the theatre is just a terrible passing phase.

JOE. I'm sure he's very proud really.

NINA. I hoped he would be if he came to see it. It was my first proper part.

JOE. Still I expect your husband gives you his support?

NINA. Yeah, he does in his way.

JOE. I'm sorry . . . does he live very far away?

NINA. He's dead. It's alright. It's just one of those things. One of those ghastly, bloody awful things.

JOE. Was he ill?

NINA. No, it was much more stupid and absurd than that. He was a fighter pilot, really. A great dancer and a very good fighter pilot. But he crashed. A mid-air collision at tremendous speed. A one in a million chance. In the lake district. It was a beautiful day. But then I suppose it usually is. Not that it makes it any easier.

JOE. How old was he?

NINA. Thirty-three. Christ died at thirty-three. Rather more painfully I suppose.

JOE. What did you do when it happened?

NINA. Went to pieces. The usual. And then after a while you start to put life back together again. Martin always used to say that 'Life is a silly old business – you fall down, you get up, you fall down, you get up.' Literally in my case.

JOE. And had you always been in the theatre?

NINA. Oh no, always in the services. Service family. R.A.F. Of course. Theatre was all a lot of nonsense, spare time stuff if you had to. Martin was different though. He always believed I could be a grown-up actress.

JOE. I think you're a very grown-up actress.

> *Cut.*

48   INT. CHURCH – DAY.

> *Rehearsal montage.* HENRY *in full dramatic flow as Claudius.*

HENRY. 'Oh, my offence is rank.' (*He sinks dramatically to his knees with great speed. Mistake.*) Ah! Can we rehearse on something harder?

> *Beat on* JOE's *reaction.*

> *Cut.*

> NINA *in moustache, beard and glasses as an attendant, is acting with* TERRY, *as the Queen. The moustache flaps up and down as she speaks.*

TERRY. 'So full of artless jealousy is guilt,
It spills itself in fearing to be splilt.
Sin fliling to be flit,'

Oh God, if I go through that sentence again I'll lose a filling.

> *Cut.*

> *Close-up on* JOE's *weary face as we hear the sounds of the play off screen.*

> *Cut.*

43

VERNON and MOLLY in the closet scene. MOLLY is in the act of killing VERNON, who is hidden behind a screen.

MOLLY. 'Dead, dead for a ducat, dead.'

After a series of stangulated 'aaagh's' VERNON emerges with a comedy half-sword wired around his head.

VERNON. Where would you like it love, when I stagger out dramatically from behind the arras? It could be anywhere with Hamlet. At this stage he hardly knows his arras from his elbow.

VERNON *and* MOLLY. Ho, ho.

Cut.

Close up on TOM as Fortinbras. TOM has become Norwegian. He talks strangely.

TOM/FORTINBRAS.
'Go, Captain, from me greet the Danish King.
Tell him that by his licence Fortinbras
Craves the conveyance of a promis'd march
Over his kingdom. You know the rendezvous.'

JOE. Tom, I just . . . don't get it . . .

TOM. Norwegian, darling Norwegian . . . all those fiords and roll mop herrings, they walk differently. They talk differently.

JOE. Yes, but they do live on planet Earth.

TOM. This isn't easy Joe.

Cut.

FADGE is taking CARNFORTH through the special movement required to play both Rosencrantz and Guildenstern at the same time. It involves constant rotation, but with exaggerated movements, like Marcel Marceau after a few pints.

FADGE. And Guildenstern and Rosencrantz and Guildenstern and Rosencrantz (*She turns.*) ' My honoured lord' (*She turns again, a different voice.*) 'My most dear Lord.'

JOE. What have I done?

Cut.

49   INT. CHURCH – DAY.

The company gathered. Rather gloomily listening to
JOE's summing up.

JOE. Well . . . that was an extraordinary first week. No one said
it was would be easy. It's a big play. And we've covered every
scene . . .

HENRY (*under his breath*). In shit.

JOE. And that in itself is a great achievement . . . I think we have
to worry a little less about the exterior of these characters; clothes
and walks and accents, etc., and concentrate a little more on each
individual's needs, their drives. What is it they want and need.
Why they do what they do. Not How. The How will take care of
itself if we ask always, why, why, why?

HENRY. Believe me darling, I've been asking.

JOE. If we can use that energy, that hunger, the very hunger that's
brought us here for this unique opportunity, I think you'll find that
the play will give you back a great deal. You have to trust
yourselves . . . We have to trust ourselves. We have a great deal to
offer . . . both to each other . . . and to the audiences . . . and do
remember please, it is only the end of the first week.

HENRY. Yes, the problem is love, there is no second week. We
have four more days before the technical rehearsal. One dress
rehearsal on Christmas Eve afternoon, and on in the evening . . .

Beat.

JOE. We have set ourselves a challenge there is no doubt. But at
Shakespeare's own theatre, a six-week season would have
produced thirty-five performance of seventeen different plays
including at times four world premieres, so as Polonius says
'Sometimes Brevity can be the soul of wit'. But I don't think we
should lose our nerve.

Cut.

50   INT. HENRY and TERRY'S BEDROOM – EVENING.

HENRY and TERRY's dorm. Two camp beds (ooo er,
vicar) quite close together, copies of the play on their
laps.

TERRY. It's bloody difficult isn't it, old Sally Shakespeare?
Especially for us new girls.

HENRY. Join the club love.

TERRY. But you've done it before.

HENRY. Never. Just seems that way.

TERRY. Ooo you minx. You're full of surprises.

HENRY. I know, love, just an old bullshitter. Always wanted to do the classics, of course. Used to read about the old Shakespeare Companies. You know, eight plays in six days. Travelling from town to town on a Sunday. Hundreds of people waving the actors off from the platform. So romantic. Unfortunately I was born out of my time. When I joined the business all that was gone. It was divided in two. There was the 'proper' theatre, you know Stratford and all that, and then there was the commercial stuff. Well, a little suburban oik like me, had no chance of the tights and fluffy white shirts. I was straight into understudying old men and 'anyone for tennis?'

TERRY. So you haven't really done any Shakespeare?

HENRY. No.

TERRY. You must be a bit nervous.

HENRY. Total brown-trouser job love. But you can't show the young ones your fear. So you cover up by being a crabby old git.

TERRY. Oh, you're very convincing.

HENRY. Well we all have our crosses to bear. Mind you, you know, I do feel as though I've done it before, the classics. Through people like Irving and Tree.

TERRY. I adore Irving.

HENRY. Do you know about him?

TERRY. Darling, just 'cos I'm in a frock at the end of a pier, doesn't mean I don't have a grasp of theatrical history.

HENRY. He was amazing, wasn't he? Oik, just like me, a stammer, a limp, every disadvantage and yet the first actor ever to be knighted.

TERRY. And he died with his boots on.

HENRY. That's right in harness. On tour, in Bradford. What a way to go. (*Beat.*) Mind you I've died in Bradford a few times.

51   INT. JOE'S OFFICE – NIGHT.

> *We don't know where we are to begin with. It seems like another rehearsal scene. A close up of acting with utter conviction.*

JOE. 'O God, O God,
How weary stale, flat and unprofitable
Seem to me all the uses of this world!'

> MOLLY *leans into frame.*

MOLLY. That's not bad, Sir Laurence.

JOE. Well, I understand how he feels, Vivien.

> *He's sitting over a page of accounts.*

JOE. Oh Christ, what are we gonna do? This was all so carefully worked out. Based on a (let's face it) optimistic turn out of three hundred people a night for seven performances making an average donation . . . of –

MOLLY. Donation?

JOE. Well, we can't charge proper ticket prices, that's not what it's about, anyway, an average donation of £2.50, that is £750 per night which makes it £5,250 for the run, less £2100 for the production budget and rent, less £100 per week per person profit-share (hopefully) for three weeks for eight people, less £150 for the first night drinks and Christmas dinner, less £600 for food and utilities. Anyway, brings it all back to nothing. It certainly doesn't magic up £700 for production week rent, and in any case, that's based on the idea of a box-office advance cash from which I could borrow money, as opposed to my credit card which is now kaput.

> VERNON *has been listening.*

VERNON. Spatch to the rescue chief. (VERNON *is wearing a sandwich board advertising the production. He's also carrying leaflets.*) Fadge did the board. I ran off the flyers on my computer. I'm going to trail the streets of Hope. If you give me the tickets, I'll sell some 'live'.

JOE/MOLLY. Fantastic.

> MOLLY *hands him a book of cloakroom tickets with dates hand written across them and a little cash bag.*

VERNON. I also have a booking at Chelford Castle.

JOE. What, the ruin?

VERNON. Part ruin, part Country Hotel.

MOLLY (*to Joe*). After your time love. The beginning of the attempted yuppification of the area. A smooth blend of ancient monument and leisure facility. Didn't work.

VERNON. Ah, but the hotel does. For Christmas anyway. It's fully booked and they are about to get my occasional cabaret act, of crooning and conjuring.

JOE. And might you sell some tickets for *Hamlet*?

VERNON. Or my middle name's not 'fabulously talented and modest'.

JOE. Vernon, I love you. In a platonic way, obviously.

MOLLY. Obviously.

JOE. Although you do have a lovely ass.

> *Cut.*

52 INT. CHURCH – DAY.

> JOE, *now playing Hamlet, with some fire, and* TERRY
> *in the Closet Scene.*

TERRY. 'This is the very coinage of your brain.
This bodiless creation ecstasy is very cunning in.'

JOE. 'Ecstasy!
My pulse as yours doth temperately keep time,
And makes as healthful music. It is not madness
That I have uttered . . . Mother, for love of grace,
Lay not that flattering unction to your soul,
That not your trepass but my madness speaks
It will but skin and film the ulcerous place,
Whiles rank corruption, mining all within,
Infects unseen. Confess yourself to heaven,
Repent what's past, avoid what is to come.'

TERRY. 'Oh, Hamlet thou hast cleft my heart in twain' –

I'm sorry I can't go on

JOE (*excited*). It's terrific. It's terrific. You must, you must.
You're just avoiding confronting it as an actor that's all, that's all,
you have to feel her guilt, you have to confess to your son –

TERRY. I tried, I tried . . . he wouldn't listen.

TERRY *bursts into tears and runs from the rehearsal.*

JOE. . . . what . . . ?

VERNON. Bit close to home love.

    Cut.

53 INT. CHURCH BY STAINED WINDOW – DAY.

    HENRY *listening quietly to* TERRY.

HENRY. When?

TERRY. When I was seventeen. The only time I'd ever been with a girl. Before or since.

HENRY (*amazed*). Just once?

TERRY. I know, bull's eye. This girl wasn't firing blanks.

HENRY. What did you do?

TERRY. Well, I was already half way to running off to the circus if you know what I mean. She was determined to have the kid. Not that I'd have known what to have done even if she hadn't been. Once she found out that I kicked with the other foot she'd have nothing to do with me anyway.

HENRY. Do you know where they are?

TERRY. Oh. He found me, love. Kids do. They get a bee in their bonnet. All turn into Sherlock Holmes when it comes to their real Mummy and Daddy. Christmas Eve, Bradford as it happens, *Puss in Boots*, four years ago.

HENRY. What happened?

TERRY. Well, it was a bit like that scene we just did. Not quite such a good script. I'd abandoned him and his mother (who he hates for hiding me). He was ashamed of my job and what I was. Am. And never wanted to see me again. No surprises.

HENRY. He must have been very upset.

TERRY. So was I.

HENRY. Have you seen him since?

TERRY. Oh, I've written to him. I get the occasional card. The thing is, Henry, this play brings it back more than I thought possible. Shakespeare wasn't stupid. Families you know, they don't work do they?

HENRY. I don't know love. I've never had one, always fancied one but it never worked out . . .

TERRY. I'll never be able to go on.

HENRY. Yes you will. We both will.

Cut.

54   INT. CHURCH – NIGHT.

Everyone tired.

TOM. 'Thought and affliction, passion, hell itself
She turns to favour . . . '

CARNFORTH *staggering in.*

CARNFORTH (*interrupting*). Has anyone seen a bottle of lemonade I had with me? I've got a bit of a sore throat.

VERNON. Lemonade?

CARNFORTH. Yes, lemonade. What's your problem buster?

JOE. OK. OK, let's go again from Ophelia's song and please, please give this scene the intensity it deserves. You're all shying away from the power of this play. Now this scene is about loss. The loss of sense, Ophelia's madness, the loss of a sister, the loss of a relationship between Claudius and Gertrude, and crucially the loss, the death of someone they have all in their own ways experienced a profound love for, that's a human emotion we can all share – that's where we connect with the audience in Hope or wherever, we have to believe you have suffered such a loss – (*He starts to realise.*) I'm sorry Nina –

NINA. No, you're perfectly right Joe. We must imagine the reality of it. I'm fine.

JOE. Alright. Let's go again from that point.

> *The atmosphere changes as the tired company register the heartbreaking effort with which* NINA *starts to sing the song. A voice of such fragility and simplicity. A beautiful tune, an achingly painful moment*

NINA (*slowly*). 'And will he not come again?
And will he not come again?
No, no, he is dead,
Go to thy death bed,
He never will come again.'

Sorry.

She runs off distraught.

TOM (*quietly*). 'Do you see this, Oh God.'

> JOE *drops his head. Silence.*

> *Cut.*

55   EXT. PHONEBOX – NIGHT.

> *We cut between* JOE *and* MARGARETTA *on the telephone. She is at home decorating her Christmas Tree.*

MARGARETTA. Look darling, if I start now it will be an open drain. You've made ridiculously optimistic calculations based on an income that simply doesn't exist.

JOE. It will.

MARGARETTA. Well, when it does, I will forward some cash . . .

JOE. Have you anything exciting to tell me?

MARGARETTA. Well, it looks like Dylan's blown it, darling. They start shooting in LA on Boxing Day and she hasn't even had a costume fitting yet. The producer, Nancy Crawford, herself no less is in town recce-ing foreign locations – she is going mad.

JOE. Can't you just get me a week of his expenses?

MARGARETTA. Darling, you're under too much pressure. Why don't you take Sunday off and relax. Remember it's Christmas. You could write to Santa.

> JOE *leaves the phone box and walks slowly up the country lane.*

> *Cut.*

56   INT. CHURCH STAGE – EVENING.

> TOM *as Fortinbras.* CARNFORTH *as the Captain, now almost totally insensible.*

JOE. Let's start again.

TOM. 'Go, Captain, from me greet the Danish King –'

> *Suddenly* CARNFORTH *burps.* TOM *stops in mid-sentence. Fatigue has got the better of him. The tantrum begins.*

51

TOM (*yelling*). Sorry. I'm sorry I can't do this, darling – it's just not possible. I'm playing four hundred parts, you won't allow me to do a single accent, I've got a Captain here who can't walk in a straight line.

CARNFORTH. Hey, steady on . . .

TOM. If you could do that love, we'd be fine . . . Joe . . . I'm committed to this project 132%, you know that. Everything that I am as a human being is here. I bring it in every morning, it's yours. My energy is always positive energy, physically, intellectually and . . . thingme. But all I ever get back from people is ridicule. Let's all have a cheap joke at Tom's expense, well that's fine that really is perfectly all right, because my shoulders are broad. I . . . em . . . I've kept my own peace. . . . I haven't rung my agent.

VERNON. She hasn't got an agent.

TOM. Yes I have. . . . Shut up . Shut up, will you . . . It really isn't fair . . . It's just too . . . too much.

> *Silence.*

JOE (*weary*). I'm sorry Tom. Very sorry.

> TOM *breathes deeply.*

TOM. I'm sorry too Joe. I'm sorry everyone.

HENRY. Fine.

TOM. Vernon, please.

JOE. Start again.

> TOM *goes and hugs* CARNFORTH.

TOM. Love this man.

> TOM *prepares, comes back on and starts to speak.*
> CARNFORTH *holding on for grim death.*

TOM. 'Go, Captain, from me – (*Vernon has started filming. Tantrum man re-emerges.*) You see, it's hopeless. Absolutely hopeless. Everything we do, from wiping our ass to fluffing our lines has to be on camera. Can't we work in private for once. Why does everyone have to see behind the scenes, these days. Whatever happened to all the bloody mystery?

VERNON (*enraged, snaps*). I'm recording our history love. It was discussed, right Joe. I think it's the least I deserve. I'm the only one who's got off his ass to sell this show.

TOM. Always vulgar.

VERNON. Don't you want anyone to see it? Or would you rather just do your bloody stupid accents in front of the mirror?

> JOE *cuts across the row emerging. He is now officially at the end of his tether. Temper volcano.*

JOE. Right, that's it, that's it, that's it. That is it. That. Is. It.

> *Silence.*

TOM. What do you mean?

JOE. (*yelling*). I mean, the play's over. Finito, walk away. End of story. Kaput. Cheerio.

VERNON. Do you don't really mean that?

JOE. What is the point? What is the fucking point? I . . . look. You're a perfectly decent bunch of people. A group of actors with all the normal insecurities and vanities. But basically I know you want to be here, we all want to do what's best for the show, but look at us? We argue. We're depressed. We've set ourselves too great a target. It is too personal for us all. It's a big play and we keep running up against it and hurting ourselves, and I for one can no longer know what I'm doing or why I'm doing it. I don't know this.

NINA. That's not true.

JOE. (*even bleaker*). The miserable facts are we've run out of time to rehearse this, we have no audience, we have no design. I'm sorry Fadge but that's true, and because I do not have the money to pay for it, we do not even have this venue for the run of the show. This whole idea, oh God, I see it now, no offence Molly, it's just pointless. Churches close and theatres close every week because finally people don't want them. The Hope Hamlet is a loser, led by the chief loser, yours truly, and circumstances just force me to ask myself, not only what is the point of carrying on this meaningless shambles, but as the Yuletide season takes us in its grip I ask myself what is the point in going on with this miserable tormented life? I mean can anyone tell me, please, please, what makes this fucking life worth living?

> *Long silence. They are stunned. Eventually.*

TOM. I think you're just projecting negativity and I think it's really unfair on Fadge.

FADGE. It's alright Tom.

> *Beat.*

VERNON. Rachmaninov.

JOE. What?

VERNON. That bit in *Brief Encounter*. And *Brief Encounter* actually. That makes life worth living. I'll buy you the video for Christmas.

>*Beat.*

TERRY. Thinking of Tim being happy.

VERNON. Who's Tim?

TERRY. My son.

>*Beat.*

CARNFORTH. Oh shit. Do we all have to do one?

VERNON. Shut up Carnforth.

>*Beat.*

HENRY. Look. Joe, I might be speaking out of turn but I feel, I think we all feel, that . . . well some of what you say is true but . . . we've come such a long way . . . it's certainly worth one more go . . . Why don't we call it a night and have one run at the play tomorrow morning. At least do that . . . eh . . . ? Just for us . . . eh . . . boss?

>*JOE nods. They are still very quiet. MOLLY lets out a little sound.*

JOE. What is it Moll?

MOLLY (*lip trembling*). You. You're my brother. You make life worth living. You make my life worth living. So don't say it's not – (*She breaks down.*)

>*He rushes to her. Hugs her . . .*

>*Cut.*

57 INT. CHURCH – DAY.

>*Final Run Montage. Assorted scenes. CARNFORTH starts off it off, scaring them all shitless with:*

CARNFORTH. 'Who's there?'

>*Noël Coward bursts into song.*

>*Cut.*

54

HENRY *in stirring, stern form as Claudius.*

HENRY. 'And we beseech you, bend you to remain
Here in the cheer and comfort of our eye,
Our chiefest courtier, cousin and our son.'

> *Cut.*

> *Close ups of the intense fascinated faces of the watching company. It's all starting to happen!*

> *Cut.*

> JOE *in inspiring form, chills his audience.*

JOE. 'Bloody, bawdy villain!
Remorseless, treacherous, lecherous, kindless villain,
O Vengeance!'

> *Cut.*

> NINA, *tragic, real.*

NINA. 'O, what a noble mind is here o'erthrown.'

> *Cut.*

> TOM *and* CARNFORTH *sober-ish and steady.*

TOM. ' . . . and let him know so.'

CARNFORTH. 'I will do't my Lord.'

TOM. 'Go softly on.'

> CARNFORTH *hesitates for a moment over which way to go softly, then makes a definite decision. He is wrong.*

CARNFORTH. Oh shit. Sorry.

> FADGE *gets up and leads him off.*

> *Cut.*

TERRY. ' . . . but long it could not be.
Till that her garments, heavy with their drink,
Pulled the poor wretch from her melodious lay
To muddy death.'

> *Cut.*

> *Wide Shot of the dead bodies. Last scene.*

TOM. 'Go bid the soldiers shoot!'

> *A beat, and then tremendous applause from* MOLLY *and* FADGE. JOE *leaps up. Everyone starts applauding and cheering.*

55

JOE (*running to* MOLLY *and hugging her*). That was terrific . . . it really started to come alive . . . I'm so proud of you all . . .

FADGE (*over-excited*). I'm nearly there Joe, nearly there. I haven't quite hit on the right era yet. We'll try things out during the tech but I can feel it in my nips.

TOM (*rushing up and hugging Joe*). Joe, do you realise how good you are in this. You are so bloody good.

NINA. You were fantastic.

JOE. Oh . . .

TERRY. But enough about me, darling, what did you think of my performance . . .

JOE. No . . . everybody . . . It was just . . . everything I could have hoped to see start happening . . . I just wish . . .

VERNON (*hushing everyone*). Now . . . Joe . . . before you say anything. We've talked to Moll about the financial situation and we feel, the company feels that we should help out. So anyway, we've had a whip round. Everybody's put in what they can which I'm afraid isn't nearly enough but . . .

TOM. Fadge has sold her van.

JOE. Sold the van . . . ? But you keep everything in there all your lights and costumes and props . . .

FADGE. They'll hold on to it till the new year. If the play succeeds I'll buy it back.

JOE. Oh folks . . . You mean . . . ?

MOLLY. We paid it this morning Joe. The show can go on.

    Beat. They all look at him.

JOE. I don't know what to say. I'm . . . I'm . . .

HENRY. A talentless git?

JOE. Oh yes, certainly but . . . thank you. Thank you very much. I think I'm going to cry.

NINA. Don't do that. We all have a jobs to do. The technical rehearsal is first thing tomorrow morning. And Fadge has got half of us working on lights and blacking out the windows and the rest of us are going into Hope this afternoon to find our audience.

JOE. That's fantastic.

TOM. But first we have a drink.

Loud cheers especially from CARNFORTH.

TERRY. And some music!

58   INT. CHURCH – DAY.

> *The place blacked-out as it will be for the evening
> performances. All we can see is smoke swirling around,
> and hear the noise of coughing. Eventually a bewildered*
> CARNFORTH *comes into view. He can't see a thing.*

CARNFORTH. 'Who's there?'

JOE O/S *(from the auditorium)*. No, no, remember Carnforth as we
discovered in rehearsal –

CARNFORTH. No I mean, who's there? – I can't see a thing.

JOE. Oh, sorry Carnforth. Hey, well done though, I really believed
you the second time there . . . Vernon . . . ?

> VERNON *emerges from the mist with a gong in hand.*

VERNON. Yes, love?

JOE O/S. A little more definite with the gong. It really sets up the
tone of the play.

VERNON. Well it would help, if there wasn't quite so much
smoke back her. I keep thinking I'm going to bump into Jack the
Ripper, and he's going to think I'm the man from the Rank logo.

JOE. Well, can't one of the others do the gong?

VERNON. Well, Nina's blind enough as it is without having to hit
a gong in the mist, Carnforth's on, Tom's on in a sec, you're out
there –

JOE. Well, what about Terry or Henry?

> *Cut.*

57

59   INT. DRESSING ROOM – DAY. (BLACKOUT).

> TERRY *and* HENRY *each at their dressing place.*
> *Mirrors and desks already crammed with things.*
> TERRY's *face makes a Robert Helpmann make-up look*
> *underdone.* HENRY *has gone for rouge and a juve wig.*
> *They both look grotesque, and they've hardly begun.*

TERRY. You look wonderful.

HENRY. You look gorgeous.

> *They both laugh.*

> *Cut.*

60   INT. CHURCH – DAY. (BLACKOUT).

> *Trestle table and chairs in the auditorium. Pads of paper,*
> *primitive lighting console, behind which* MOLLY *sits*
> *making notes for* JOE, *whose face is lit dramatically by*
> *an angle-poise lamp.*

JOE. Fadge?

> *Out of the gloom with a miner's helmet and fluorescent*
> *jacket emerges* FADGE *holding a box/gun from which*
> *smoke is issuing.*

FADGE. Teething problems, darling, that's why we rehearse.

JOE. Yes, sure no problem with that Fadge. It's just that we have
spent all morning on this and still haven't got beyond, 'Who's
there?' a question I fear many of the audience will be asking, if the
smoke's this thick.

FADGE. Opening image, darling, it's crucial.

JOE. Understood. Any final decision about props? Or costumes . . . ?

FADGE. I've got till the end of the tech haven't I?

JOE. Yes.

FADGE. Let's remain open.

> *Cut.*

61   INT. AUDITORIUM – AFTERNOON. (BLACKOUT).

Later that same day. MOLLY *and* JOE *at their console.*

JOE. Alright then let's go from the last line of the previous scene, ready to bring on the throne. Tom, give us your last line, you can say it from off-stage for now. Stand by LX and stand by sound. And . . . Cue Tom.

TOM O/S. 'Let's do't, I pray, and I this morning know where we shall find him most convenient.'

JOE. Go LX, Go Music . . . (*They go.*) . . . that's good . . . Vernon on first that's right, check out the audience as if seeing our imaginary court, excellent. Very good to hold her hand . . . Keep her out of trouble, that's good . . . and now the King and Qu –

> *He stops in mid sentence to take in what has appeared.*
> TERRY *and* HENRY *look like something from the*
> *Lyceum circa 1885. Both think their characters are*
> *twenty-three years-old. Both are unsuccessfully trying*
> *to prove this.*

TERRY. What you think darling?

HENRY. Not bad eh?

JOE. OK. Just . . . Let's just hold it there . . . erm do you know this is not a bad time to have an informal chat about costume and make-up . . . Let's break for tea there, back in an hour . . . Um . . . Henry and Terry . . . a little word in your ear.

HENRY. What's wrong with him?

TERRY. Don't know love, this is as good as it fucking gets.

HENRY. If he don't like this, he don't like anything.

TERRY. Fuck her, darling.

> CARNFORTH *appears at* JOE's *side.*

CARNFORTH. Joe, could you call your agent.

JOE. What? I'll be right with you.

CARNFORTH. I just popped down to the post office, And the landlord said there was a message for you to call your agent.

JOE. The landlord? At the post office.

CARNFORTH. Yes, it's a technical term, I believe . . . came in with privatisation . . . anyway . . . urgent

JOE. Wait a minute, its the day before Christmas eve, there are no agents working.

CARNFORTH. Oh yes, that's it, could you call her at home. Is there a message . . . ? I could always pop back and have another . . .

JOE. I think you should work on your rotational movement exercises.

>*Beat.*

Carnforth. Don't drink. You don't need to.

>*Cut.*

62   INT. CHURCH – TEA-TIME.

>*The entrance hall area.* VERNON *and* MOLLY *sit at a table with the seating plan for the first night and tickets. In the background* FADGE *and* CARNFORTH *are practising his rotational exercises.*

VERNON. So, how many does that make?

MOLLY. Well,I've got a party of ten kids from the school coming down. £3 a head. Most of them will have a bloody miserable Christmas anyway.

VERNON. What, so you mean so even this pile of old toss is better than nothing?

MOLLY. NO! But . . .

VERNON. Only teasing. (*He sits down.*) I won't know till tomorrow night about the crowd from Chelford Castle. They're a bit over-excited.

MOLLY. Why?

VERNON. They've got this film company coming to do a location recce there tomorrow morning. Very last minute but if they use the castle, the hotel's the best place to put the crew in. Quids in for the landlord.

MOLLY. At last.

VERNON. Exactly, so you can imagine, Hamlet is a little lower on his list of priorities. We could do with his crowd tomorrow night, mind you. It would swell the coffers. Anyway I'm still working him over.

MOLLY. How?

VERNON. Well, this film is futuristic apparently. They are doing the interiors in America and cheap locations in Europe. They want the castle to be the ruins of an ancient city on the planet Zarbok.

MOLLY. Mmmm . . . sounds lovely.

VERNON. So I told him to greet the film producer in an R2-D2 party hat and a home-made Star Trek uniform.

MOLLY. He loves Crimplene.

VERNON. Exactly.

MOLLY (*she loses her place*). Oh, flipping heck! (*He takes over.*) Thanks for doing all this Vernon. You've been a rock. It's the weirdest Christmas holiday from school I've ever spent. Every time I think I'm going slightly potty, I just look at you . . . I mean, nothing seems to phase you.

VERNON. Well, it doesn't if you're needed. I like being needed. It's a new experience for me. I should make a film about it. Being needed.

MOLLY. Can I be in it?

> *Cut.*

63   EXT. PHONE BOX/COUNTRY LANE *and* AGENT'S FLAT – LATE AFTERNOON.

> MARGARETTA *is on a treadmill wearing a headpiece telephone system and a leotard. She is eating sausages and dipping them into tomato ketchup as she exercises in front of the television.* JOE *listening to* MARGARETTA, *open-mouthed with astonishment.*

MARGARETTA. It is astonishing darling . . . only Nancy Crawford can afford to do it . . . of course it makes sense in the long run, but it's true. They want you for the three pictures guaranteed. Guaranteed Joe.

JOE. . . . But what if . . .

MARGARETTA. They have to pay you darling . . . even if they don't make the second two . . . You get more up front but no back end and I'm going to fight for a cut of the merchandising. Of course, we can't hold them to ransom if the first picture's a monster hit, but we do get three years' money and six months a year employment guaranteed, in a movie concept that could be *Star Wars* all over again.

JOE. And you're certain Dylan Judd is out of the picture?

MARGARETTA. Darling, she has shot herself in the foot, the bottom, and most crucially the brain . . . so greedy . . . And remember they still had that video tape of your audition from all those months ago. They need character for these side-kick roles, particularly if you're in a suit and latex for all those hours.

JOE. Oh my God . . . I'm speechless . . . (*Telephone pips start.*) Oh Christ look Mags, I'm going to have to run . . . Can we talk about this when you come down. Look I'll see you at the show . . . Thanks Mags . . .

> *In his haste he does not replace the receiver properly.*
> *We hear MARGARETTA on the other end of the line.*

MARGARETTA (*panicked*). . . . but Joe, we have to talk, we have to talk, start dates, travel arrangements . . . Joe, JOE.

> *Cut.*

64   INT. TERRY and HENRY'S BEDROOM – NIGHT.

> *Both in bed miserable. JOE appears at the curtain/wall of their dorm with two glasses of champagne.*

JOE. Peace offering.

> *He puts the glasses on their bedside table.*

JOE. I think you're both fantastic.

TERRY. Naughty girl.

HENRY. Bad person.

JOE. Now you trust me on this make-up issue. You'll look great.

> *He goes. They pick up their champagne.*

TERRY. He's right of course, we did look like two silly old tarts. We can't make time stand still Henry. Those days are gone forever.

HENRY. I suppose so. Fun though wasn't it?

TERRY. Oh yes, it was fun.

> *Cut.*

65   INT. CARNFORTH/VERNON'S BEDROOM – NIGHT.

> CARNFORTH *still learning lines.* VERNON *brings in two glasses of champagne. He passes one to Carnforth.*

CARNFORTH. What's all this then?

VERNON. Bribe from the boss.

CARNFORTH. This is very sporting of him.

VERNON. Yes, do you think it's the equivalent of Nero fiddling while Rome burned?

CARNFORTH. Oh hardly.

VERNON. Only joking Carnforth. Lighten up.

CARNFORTH. Well, I suppose I would love, if I didn't feel such an eight billion per cent twit.

VERNON. Still having a problem remembering the lines are we?

CARNFORTH. The lines, the movement, the costume changes, my bloody awful acting, Betty Bottle.

> *Cut.*

66   INT. CHURCH – WEE SMALL HOURS.

> FADGE *working at one end of the church, painting.*

TOM. What are you doing?

FADGE. I'm making an audience.

TOM. I beg your pardon?

FADGE. Well. I've been completely pathetic up to now but I think I'm onto something at last. If we don't get an actual audience. I want to create a World for you. You should at least have people watching you. Even if they are cardboard.

TOM. That'll be brilliant. They won't cough. I hate that.

> *Cut.*

67   INT. CHURCH – WEE SMALL HOURS.

> JOE's *office.* NINA, MOLLY *and* JOE *carving thick candles and fixing them into a great candelabra.*

NINA. Ooo I think that champagne's gone right to my head. Is this wise before a first night?

JOE. These are unusual circumstances.

MOLLY. Yes, is your bank manager drunk too?

JOE. I think, he was encouraged by some Christmas good news, to review my overdraft.

MOLLY. What you mean, someone's bought a ticket who doesn't know us or he is actually drunk?

JOE. All in good time. Let's get the show on first before I share the glad tidings.

    Cut.

68   INT. CHURCH – WEE SMALL HOURS.

    FADGE *and* TOM *laugh.*

FADGE. It's good to have a laugh, isn't it?

TOM. Oh yes.

FADGE. On the whole we've got serious disease.

TOM. I know, I know. But we are being treated for it. We did take this job. Fadge, I think I could be funny with you.

FADGE. I think you are funny with me. In fact I think we're funny with each other. Come on, let's get back to being humourless and intense. We have an audience to write and reviews to make.

    They set about work.

    Cut.

69   INT. CARNFORTH/VERNON'S BEDROOM – NIGHT.

VERNON. The problem with you, is it's so easy. It drives me mad.

CARNFORTH. Easy? What do you mean easy?

    Beat.

VERNON. I love you.

CARNFORTH. What?

VERNON. I love you.

CARNFORTH. Now Vernon, don't think I'm not flattered, it's just . . .

VERNON (*laughs*). No, no as an audience member, I love you. As a company member, I love you. As a human being, I love you. I can't help it. You've got charm, warmth, you're endearing, your honest about yourself, about your faults, your insecurities. I can't do anything about it. I love you and I've loved you ever since the first time I saw you. The audience can't help themselves either, you walk on, they love you. Because you're yourself. You're kind and vulnerable and . . . well . . . nice.

CARNFORTH. Do you really think so?

VERNON. I do. But you're so racked with guilt about your old Ma's sacrifices, that you don't even notice the audience rather likes you, or even that you're a very good actor.

> CARNFORTH *thinks.*

CARNFORTH. Well . . . I . . . suppose not. No.

VERNON. So, I wouldn't worry too much about tomorrow Carnforth.

> *Cut.*

70 INT. CHURCH – WEE SMALL HOURS.

NINA. Well I think I must be off now to Bedfordshire. (*She goes to the wrong door.*) Wrong way. (*Nearly walking into a table.*) Oops, nearly. Night.

> *She exits.*

MOLLY. I think you should take her with you.

JOE. Where?

MOLLY. Wherever you go. Wherever.

> *Cut.*

71 EXT. CHURCH. WIDE SHOT – MORNING.

> FADGE *madly pacing, with an armful of books.*

FADGE. This is it. Yes, yes. I've got it now, that's right. I've got it. I can make a decision. Of course, I can, of course I can – I can make a decision. That's it, got it. Yes, Lord. GO FOR IT.

72   INT. CHURCH – MORNING. (BLACKOUT).

> *Close-up on* TOM *yelling through the smoke as Fortinbras.*

TOM. DARLING, IT IS A NIGHTMARE!

> JOE *is at the console.*

JOE (*very cheerful*). Tom, we're fine, we're fine. It's a technical – they're always like this. Don't worry. We'll go again from the entrance, we'll lighten up on the smoke, it'll be alright.

> TERRY *and* HENRY *are in the wings, observing this.*

TERRY. Ooo Martha Moany Guts has changed her tune since yesterday, hasn't she?

HENRY. Well he's happy now we all look like TV weathermen.

> *Cut.*

73   INT. CHURCH – LATE AFTERNOON.

> *End of the dress rehearsal. Everyone on stage.*

> JOE *addresses the company.*

JOE. Alright, not bad at all. Listen, we were nice and relaxed. Technically it was remarkably smooth. Fantastic. Well done Molly and Nina and everyone who's helping out with special effects and moving things. That's great.

> *A noise from the back of the church.* JOE *turns.*

MARGARETTA. Joe, Joe, I'm so glad I've found you.

JOE. Hello Mags . . . you're early. We don't go up till 7.30 . . .

> *She rushes up to him.*

JOE. Look everyone, this is Margaretta D'arcy, my friend, agent and personal investor in the show.

MARGARETTA (*whispering*). Darling, I've got to talk to you.

JOE. What?

MARGARETTA. Got to talk to you.

JOE. Yeah. OK. Sure. Moll, do the technical notes will you . . . I'll be with you in two minutes. Two minutes.

> *He goes back to the church doors with MARGARETTA, who immediately engages him in an intense whispered conversation. We hear MOLLY's notes as we see in close up NINA's face as she watches the pair whispering. We see her P.O.V. As MOLLY finishes, JOE and MARGARETTA come down to the front.*

MOLLY. . . . so it's up to you Vernon to take off the throne before the fight starts OK?

VERNON. Fine. No problem.

> *The Company quieten as it is clear JOE has something to say. They're expecting their last rallying cry for the first performance. He begins slowly. He seems to be in shock, tense, uneasy.*

JOE. . . . I've . . . an important announcement to make . . . after over a year of spectacular unemployment during which as I'm sure you've all gathered, I've been pretty desperate, I not only have a job, but really The Job. Yes . . . a guaranteed three picture deal in a new science fiction movie trilogy . . . the bad news . . . the bad news . . .

> MARGARETTA *interrupts.*

MARGARETTA. I'm sorry, darlings. I'm going to have to be the heavy here. The bad news is, that Joe has to leave tonight.

> *Shocked silence.*

MOLLY. Tonight?

MARGARETTA. Yes, the producer, Nancy Crawford, is in the country recce-ing foreign locations. She has a private jet leaving Chelford Aerodome at 8 o'clock. They start shooting interiors in Los Angeles on Boxing Day. It couldn't be more last-minute. It's a wonderful opportunity for Joe. And there really isn't a choice. I'm sure you'll all understand but there really is no choice.

> *Long pause. They are all dumbfounded. Eventually. Slowly.*

HENRY. Well . . . she's right, Joe . . . There is no choice . . . You've got to go . . .

> *Beat.*

VERNON. Congratulations boss. You've saved the world from my nose, just in time.

Beat.

JOE. I'm sorry Vernon.

Beat.

TOM. There is no justice and I hate you passionately. Go for it, you swine.

Beat.

FADGE. I'm sure you'll get the chance to do it again Joe, but just in case, I wanted to let you know that I had finally cracked it.

The cast start to leave. Then.

NINA. Don't go. Please don't go.

HENRY. Now come on N –

NINA. He can't . . . He mustn't go. Not just for us, but for him.

TERRY. Darling there's just no comparison –

NINA. Yes, there is. Two weeks ago we all met up to start this adventure and much though we didn't care to admit it we were all in our various ways depressed, especially you Joe. We needed this job, this play, this experience. And all through our ups and downs and disagreements we've continued to need it.

JOE. Yes, we do, Nina, actors do, but the world doesn't. Finally it's Shakespeare and nobody's interested.

NINA. They're interested in Hope.

MARGARETTA. Look this is all very good and all very over-dramatic. But it just isn't fair. You can do this bloody play any-time – anywhere.

TOM. Look, Nina, Joe's only doing what most of us would give our right arms to do.

JOE. It means I can pay you all. It can be proper.

NINA. It doesn't have to be proper.

JOE. It's Christmas Eve, for Christ sake you should all be with your families.

NINA. We're with our family. That's what actors do. That's what people do in what's left of Hope. They hang on, they stick it out. Now, they're here tonight for us and we have to do the show for them and if you won't do it . . . then . . . then . . .

MOLLY. Then I'll bloody well do it. I'll play Hamlet, I practically know it now. It's better than cancelling. Everyone knows it's a weird production. One more weirdo won't make a difference. This is our village. It's our home. We can't let them down.

MARGARETTA. Well that's marvellous then isn't it?

> *Pause.*

HENRY. We are all tired and emotional . . . you get off and catch that plane . . . we'd all do the same whatever we say now. We're actors, we're beggars that's the way it works. We'll do the show tonight with young Mistress Molly and we'll drink your health over Christmas dinner tomorrow.

> TERRY *goes to* JOE *and kisses him on the cheek.*

TERRY. Get a suntan.

> FADGE *goes to* JOE *to take back his costume.*

FADGE. Sorry, Joe.

> *The rest start moving off.* NINA *remains on stage with* CARNFORTH. *All the others have disappeared backstage.*

JOE. Nina . . . I . . .

NINA. You put your whole life into this Joe. Right from the start. You needed this job. You needed it then and you need it now. It's not about fame or money or so-called wealth and security, it's about nourishing your soul, nourishing your heart. And that's what you deserve. At the end of the day however hard you hug that pay cheque, it won't be a person . . . it won't be us . . . it won't be me.

> *She runs off in tears.*

> CARNFORTH *remains. He and* JOE *stare at each other.*

CARNFORTH. Easy on yourself old chap. I'm afraid we can't all afford the luxury of nourishing our souls. That's the prerogative of the romantics among us, I fear. These things happen. What does he say, 'If it be now 'tis not to come, if it be not to come it will be now, if it be not now, yet it will come, the readiness is all'.

> JOE *is left, shell-shocked, with* MARGARETTA, *who puts an arm around him and walks him slowly back towards the door as we*

> *Cut.*

NINA *pursued by* HENRY.

HENRY. Nina. Listen. He's only human. If that had been me at his age, I wouldn't even have stopped to tell the company. I'd be on my way to the airport.

NINA. Yes, but he'd worked so hard.

HENRY. And so have you, which is why you mustn't let a beautiful performance like yours be spoiled because you're head over heels in love.

NINA. Who said I was in love? I just want what's best for him. What's best for the company.

HENRY. What's best for the company is if you go out there and give the best Ophelia the world's ever seen.

NINA. Yes, but he won't be there to see it.

HENRY. D'you think love's about always being in the same place at the same time?

NINA. It helps.

HENRY. So is doing your best for your loved one wherever they are. It's much harder for him than it is for you, if you'll pardon my language.

> *Beat. They hug.*

HENRY. What does your Dad say?

NINA. He wasn't in.

HENRY. Well if I was your Dad I'd say, 'Do this one for Joe, think of him and the pain he's in, and make him proud up there in his rather lonely aeroplane.'

> *She looks at him lovingly.*

NINA. You've turned into an old sweetie haven't you?

HENRY. No, I'm still a miserable git. And this is all a front to stop you from messing up my performance.

NINA. Alright, I'll think about it you miserable old tart.

> *They hug.*

NINA. Push off.

> *Cut.*

75   INT. BACKSTAGE DRESSING ROOM – NIGHT.

> MOLLY, *now in a state of shock, in front of the mirror, being made up by* CARNFORTH *and* TOM. *Book in hand, mumbling lines to herself incoherently. Starting to shake.*

TOM. This is so amazing, Molly, you're actually living the actor's nightmare. We all have it darling. Dreaming about going on in a major role, totally unprepared. It's so exciting.

MOLLY. Thanks Tom. Oh God, whoever said actors were sissies. I don't know how you do it. I feel sick.

CARNFORTH. Don't worry lovely. If I ever forget my lines in Shakespeare I always say, 'Crouch we here awhile and lurk'. Always seems to do the trick.

MOLLY. Why, what happens?

CARNFORTH. Well, nothing normally but, you know, provides a moment of intrigue. Gives you a chance to think of something or pick up the script, maybe.

TOM. The fight! If it all goes wrong, um . . . drop the sword and take this off and throw it at me. (*He puts a boot in her right hand.*) Then I say, 'The boot,the boot was poisoned', and die. That should work.

> MOLLY *goes green.*
>
> *Cut.*

77   INT. FRONT OF HOUSE – NIGHT.

> FADGE *is weird.* VERNON *is putting out the last of the chairs. People have started to arrive.* FADGE *tears the tickets.*

AUDIENCE MEMBER. Hello!

FADGE. Lovely. Anywhere you like. Thank you. Would you like a programme?

AUDIENCE MEMBER. Yes please.

FADGE. I'm sorry we don't have any.

> *She laughs hysterically. The mad-ometer is hitting 11.*

VERNON (*whispering*). Yes, we do.

FADGE (*loud*). Yes, we do.

> VERNON *passes them to her.*

VERNON. That'll be 50p, thank you.

FADGE. That'll be 50p, thank you.

AUDIENCE MEMBER. Any ice-cream?

FADGE. We have herbal teas, natural fruit juice, organic rice cakes with balsamic chocolate, and . . . straw.

AUDIENCE MEMBER. But, any ice-cream?

FADGE. What are you, a fascist?

VERNON (*whispering again*). Fadge, I've got the ice-cream. Here in the cool box.

FADGE. Vernon, you're a star. (*To the audience member.*) Yes, they're here. (*Sells them.*)

Vernon, you're a star. I'm completely out of my depth here. The paint's still wet on the throne, Joe's costume won't fit Molly, the smoke machine is probably down at the boozer with Carnforth having a quick one before the show. If I was any more nervous, I'd be very very nervous.

VERNON. You're doing wonderfully well, but tell me are your nipples hard?

FADGE. If they were any harder, Tom could do chin-ups from them.

> *Cut.*

78   INT. BACKSTAGE DRESSING ROOM – NIGHT.

> CARNFORTH *kisses* TERRY *good luck.* TOM *crosses the screen trying to knot his tie . . . Manic activity all around him.*

TOM. False economy not having a dresser.

> *Cut.*

79   INT. FRONT OF HOUSE – NIGHT.

> *A* YOUNG MAN *sits into shot in the rapidly filling auditorium.* FADGE *wild in the background. The*

YOUNG MAN *sits quietly and studies his programme.*
A distinguished WOMAN *in middle age sits next to him.*
A beat, then

WOMAN. My son's in this. Playing about fifteen different roles.
One of them good we hope.

MAN. Really? My Dad's in it too.

WOMAN. What's he playing?

A moment.

MAN. I'm not sure.

Cut.

80 INT. BACKSTAGE DRESSING ROOM – NIGHT.

Off screen we hear FADGE's *'One minute please, one*
minute ladies and gentlemen'. The company wait
nervously in the wings. MOLLY *being helped by* NINA
and VERNON. *Close-ups on them all.* TERRY *holds*
HENRY's *hand and whispers to himself.*

TERRY. It is a far, far better thing that I do now than I did that
night with the sailor and the artichoke.

HENRY. Oh hush Mother. Be wonderful.

Beat. They all look at each other. No more to say.
CARNFORTH *is the only one who seems rather relaxed.*

CARNFORTH (*cheerily*). They love me you know.

The audience starts to hush. The lights are starting to go
down.

Cut.

81 INT. AUDITORIUM – NIGHT.

Heads turn as MARGARETTA *obsequiously ushers in*
NANCY CRAWFORD, *film producer and undoubted*
star. She walks down the aisle, like . . . well . . . a star.
We track with them. NANCY *is accompanied by a small*
entourage, including a man with a notebook.

MARGARETTA (*grovelling*). That's the beauty of private planes
darling isn't it? They wait for you. We're all so thrilled.

73

NANCY. Does this guy bother you?

MARGARETTA. No.

NANCY. What is your name?

MAN. Mortimer.

NANCY. He's doing a profile on me for the London *Times*. That's a good paper, isn't it?

MARGARETTA. The best.

NANCY. He figured it would be good to cover me catching some art.

> *They sit down.* NANCY *sits next to one of* FADGE's *cardboard people. Nancy looks at him.*

NANCY. These are neat. We should take some of those and use them when we preview the movie.

> MARGARETTA *laughs. Then smoke covers the pair. The lights go down. The drum begins.*

82   INT. CHURCH – NIGHT.

> *Wide shot of the stage. Enter* CARNFORTH *through the smoke. For the first time, it really is rather scary. He moves slowly, almost in slow-motion then, with great swiftness he turns round firing a machine gun over the heads of the audience. The sound is terrifying.*

CARNFORTH. 'Who's there?

> *Great gasps. Close-up of riveted children's faces.*
>
> *Cut.*

83   INT. CHURCH STAGE – NIGHT.

> *The first Court Scene in progress.* HENRY *commanding and good.* MOLLY, *with her back to the audience is in shadow and to the side of the stage. The audience can barely see her. She is aquiver with nerves as the dreaded first line approaches.*

HENRY. ' . . . But now my cousin Hamlet and my son'

From the back of the auditorium, by the doors, a strong voice emerges from the gloom.

JOE. 'A little more than kin and less than kind.'

A little 'Ah' from the audience. Once again they have been taken by surprise. This is turning out to be rather good. The scene continues as MOLLY *is pulled off the stage.* HENRY *and* TERRY *are clearly delighted, as they instantly adjust the staging to deal with* JOE's *new entrance.*

HENRY. 'How is it that the clouds still hang on thee?'

JOE climbs onto the stage.

JOE. 'Not so my Lord, I am too much i'th'sun.'

This is too much for TERRY, *who, as Gertrude, flings himself, a welter of emotion, at the surprised* JOE.

TERRY. 'Good Hamlet, cast off thy coloured nightie and let thine eye look like a friend on Denmark.'

He/she hugs him ferociously as we cut to NANCY CRAWFORD *throwing* MARGARETTA *a quizzical look in the auditorium. Did he just say that?*

Cut.

84   INT. BACKSTAGE – NIGHT. A LITTLE LATER.

TOM beside himself with excitement. From onstage we hear the sounds of Hamlet and Horatio talking about the ghost. The others rushing around as ever.

TOM. Darling, darlings, Dorothy Drama has come to live with us in a big way. Nancy Crawford has delayed her flight to see her new boy in action and she's got *The Times* with her. We're going to be reviewed darling by a national newspaper!

NINA. So he's just come back for the one performance?

TOM. Be reasonable Nina. He's saved the show. Saved giving Molly a nervous breakdown and saved us the chance of a wonderful notice.

NINA. I think it's shameful.

>At that point, the previous scene ends and JOE comes off
>to the whispered congrats of CARNFORTH and
>VERNON. JOE sees her.

JOE. Nina, I . . .

>She rushes past, deliberately ignoring him.
>
>Cut.

85   INT. CHURCH AUDITORIUM – NIGHT.

>The console. MOLLY, now changed back into normal
>clothes, sits down beside FADGE.

MOLLY (mock annoyance). I was going to be rather good I
thought.

FADGE. You knelt beautifully.

>She pours a measure of whisky into MOLLY's mug. And
>takes a swig herself out of a small bottle of whisky.
>
>Cut.

86   INT. CHURCH – NIGHT.

>JOE runs down the centre aisle towards the back doors
>straight to camera.

JOE. 'Bloody, bawdy villian!
Remorseless, treacherous, lecherous, kindless villain!'

87   INT. CHURCH – NIGHT.

>FADGE and MOLLY clink glasses.
>
>Cut.

88   INT. STAGE – NIGHT.

>The Nunnery Scene. Playing beautifully. Charged with
>emotion. It's the first time JOE and NINA have spoken to
>each other.

NINA. 'Good my Lord,
How does your honour for this many a day?'

JOE. 'I humbly thank you, well, well, well'.

NINA. 'My lord, I have remembrances of yours
That I have longed to re-deliver.
I pray you now receive them'

JOE. 'No, not I, I never gave you aught.'

NINA. 'My honoured lord, you know right well you did,
And with them words of so sweet breath compared
As made the things more rich. Their perfume lost,
Take these again, for to the noble mind
Rich gifts wax poor when givers prove unkind.
There, my lord.'

> *With that she gives him an almighty belt around the face.*
> *The audience gasps.*
>
> *Cut.*

89   INT. DRESSING ROOM – NIGHT.

> NINA *storms through the dressing room, past a lot of*
> *camp raised eyebrows: 'Oooooo'.*
>
> *Cut.*

90   INT. STAGE – NIGHT.

> *Later. The play going very well, montage of bits showing*
> *everyone acting as well as they ever have, utterly real.*

JOE. 'Madam, how like you this play?'

TERRY. 'The lady doth protest too much me thinks'

JOE. 'O, but she'll keep her word'

HENRY. 'Have you heard the argument? Is there on offence in't?'

JOE. 'No, no, they do but jest, poison in jest, no offence i'th' world'

HENRY. 'What do you call the play?'

JOE. 'The Mousetrap'.

*Uneasy laughter from the court and audience. We feature
a close-up reaction on* TERRY'S SON *and*
CARNFORTH'S MOTHER, *both rapt.*

Cut.

The Closet Scene.

TERRY. 'What wilt thou do? Thou wilt not murder me? Help,
help, Ho!'

VERNON. 'What ho! Help, help, help!'

JOE. 'How now, a rat? Dead, for a ducat, dead.'

> JOE *thrusts his sword through a sheet, which
> dramatically pours blood.*

> *Cut.*

TERRY. 'Calmly, good Laertes.'

> TOM *sweaty and butch holding* HENRY *at sword's
> length.*

TOM (*savagely*).
'That drop of blood that's calm proclaims me bastard.'

> *Close up on* NANCY CRAWFORD.

NANCY. He's good.

MARGARETTA. He's with me.

NANCY. What's his name?

> MARGARETTA *hastily looks in the programme.*

MARGARETTA. Nina . . . NEWMAN, TOM NEWMAN.

> *Cut.*

91   INT. BACKSTAGE – NIGHT.

> VERNON *rushing through, still with his bald cap and
> sword through his body, from Polonius's death.*

VERNON. . . . . put the champagne on ice, love. Joe will need a
bottle on a drip feed directly into the vein . . . If it had been any
closer he would have nearly got me . . . Where's the toilet?

> *Cut.*

92   INT. STAGE – NIGHT.

> JOE *in brilliant form, soliloquizing. Hamlet's pain and weariness all too clear.*

JOE. 'What is a man if his chief good and market of his time be but to sleep and feed, a beast no more.'

> *Cut.*

> *We pan across the excited faces of the audience as we hear the frightening sounds of the sword fight. Clangs and gasps and cheers.*

> *Cut.*

> *Hamlet's Death. A thick silence.*

JOE. 'The rest is silence.'

CARNFORTH.
'Now cracks a noble heart. Good night sweet prince.
And flights of angels sing thee to thy rest.'

> *Close on* CARNFORTH'S MUM. *Very proud.*

> *Cut.*

93 INT. CHURCH – NIGHT.

> *Close on the audience as we hear Fortinbras's now familiar line*

TOM. 'Go, bid the soldiers shoot.'

> *Darkness. Drum. Gong. Then. Wild applause. The place in an uproar. Darlings it's a TRIUMPH. We track along the faces of the company as they take their bows. Ecstatic.* FADGE *and* MOLLY *join the cast to take a bow.*

> *Cut.*

94   INT. BACKSTAGE – NIGHT.

> *Champagne pops, campery erupts, total hysteria.*

VERNON. No you were marhvellous daarhling.

CARNFORTH. Noooo, yoou were marvhellous daaarling.

VERNON. No, you were –

MOLLY. Carnforth?

>CARNFORTH *has stopped camping. His* MOTHER *has arrived with* MOLLY. CARNFORTH *can hardly speak.*

CARNFORTH. Mum . . . were you? . . . did you? . . .

MRS BRANCH. I'm afraid I did. And I'm very cross with you.

CARNFORTH. Really?

MRS BRANCH. Yes, you broke my heart as Horatio. I was in tears most of the evening.

CARNFORTH. Really?

MRS BRANCH. Yes.

VERNON. Would you like a drink Mrs . . .

MRS BRANCH. Yes, please.

>FADGE *rushes in.*

FADGE. It's a triumph. Excuse me, God you were good, wasn't he?

MRS BRANCH. Yes.

CARNFORTH. Fadge, our designer.

>*Cut.*

95 INT. DRESSING ROOMS – NIGHT.

>TERRY *in his place.* HENRY *enters, with* TIM.

HENRY. Terry, visitor for you.

TERRY. Christ.

>*Pause.*

TIM. Hello, Dad. Henry dropped me a line. Told me what you were up to.

TERRY. Well, it's not quite *Puss in Boots* in Bradford is it?

TIM. You were very good in that. I'm sure it's just as hard to do panto.

TERRY. Oh, it is love, but a bit easier on the heart strings though. How's your . . . ?

TIM. She's very well. She sends her best.

TERRY. Really?

TIM. Really. We both got quite a turn from Henry's letter. I . . . we both thought it was time to be a little more . . . well, I'm just very glad I saw it. I think you're a wonderful queen, in every way.

TERRY. Cheeky bugger.

> *They laugh.*

TIM. Look, I'll have to get back Christmas Eve and all . . . but I'd like to bring Ma . . . and me girlfriend . . . next week maybe? . . .

TERRY. . . . er . . . ern . . . yes . . . lovely.

TIM. Great. Well look. I'll be off. Well done, Dad . . . I thought you were great.

TERRY. Thank you

> *He gives him a hug.*

TERRY. Good boy.

> TIM *leaves.*

TIM. Thanks, Harry.

HENRY. HENRY!

> TERRY *picks up his glass of champagne.*

TERRY. Henry Wakefield, what the fuck did you put in the letter?

HENRY. I told him you had cholera.

> TERRY *spits out the drink.*
>
> *Cut.*

97   INT. AUDITORIUM – NIGHT.

> *The audience filing out.* NANCY *and* MARGARETTA *talking intently, stay where they are.*

NANCY. . . . it's better taller . . . taller and chunkier, chunky is good . . . see I can make a lot more value out of the spatial relationships.

MARGARETTA. Exactly darling, well you know Shakespeare. I mean, if you can get the spatial relationships right . . . it's . . . it's . . . often can be so much better . . .

MORTIMER. I'll go and file this. Editor's rather intrigued to have a Shakespeare review in panto season. (*To* NANCY.) Thank you.

>*He goes.*

98   INT. DRESSING ROOM – NIGHT.

>JOE *trying to talk to* NINA.

JOE. Look Nina, please let me try to explain.

>NANCY *and* MARGARETTA *approach in the background.*

NANCY. Well, if it isn't the very sad Swedish person himself.

MARGARETTA. Joe, this is Nancy Crawford.

JOE. Oh. Hello, it was very kind of you to come and see the play.

NANCY. Listen, I figure I have to check out any guy who can turn me down like that. He should be worth watching, however stupid.

NINA. You said no . . . ?

MARGARETTA. Yes, before the show, rather disproves your theory from martyr central, doesn't it?

>NINA *looks at* JOE. *Neither knows what to say.* TOM *and* FADGE *approach from behind them.*

NANCY. Still, as in all box-office hits we do have a happy ending. I'd like you all to meet the new 'Smegma'.

>*She indicates* TOM.

TOM. And my own personal costume designer.

>FADGE *beams.*

NANCY. I loved your little thin people. We're going to base Smegma's look on some of these. I mean, it was so neat. The whole thing was like a Judy Garland movie. (*To* TOM.) You're gonna be great. I mean, taller is better. He needs your kind of physique. And all those different accents. You have to get lots of character under the latex. Where are you from originally?

TOM. Norway.

NANCY. Hey, great for the European investors. Oh and don't worry honey (*To* FADGE.) I'll make sure he's naked for the first two weeks of the shoot, so you have some time for the costume concept. You're gonna love Nathan, he's a wonderful designer, he just couldn't find his Smegma.

NINA. Tom, you're playing Smegma in the new Sci-fi film *Galaxy Terminus*?

MARGARETTA. You're too quick for your own good darling.

NANCY. Well I hope he is. I don't need any more fuck-ups on this role. Do you have an 'out' in your contract?

TOM. Sorry?

NANCY. Did your agent negotiate a way for you to leave the show, should such a thing happen?

VERNON. He doesn't have an agent.

MARGARETTA (*smoothly*). Yes he does, and obviously we'll make some compensation to the management. We'll talk about it, Joe.

NANCY. Well, we have a plane to catch . . . Bob?

TOM. Tom. I'll be right along.

NANCY. Snatch?

FADGE. Fadge. Right with you boss.

NANCY (*she starts to go. Turns to NINA and JOE*). Mickey and Judy. You two were fine. Keep it up kids.

> *She goes.*

MARGARETTA (*to JOE*). For what it's worth darling. I thought you were a wonderful Hamlet.

> *She kisses him and starts to go, then stops.*

Do you have representation Snot?

FADGE. Fadge.

NANCY O/S. Margaretta!

> MARGARETTA *rushes out.*

MARGARETTA. Coming Nancy. (*She hands FADGE her card.*) Here, call me.

> *They are gone. All the actors are now gathered.*

TOM. I think I'm going to faint.

FADGE. Oh, God Joe it's alright isn't it? I mean my work's done here and Molly can just as easily fill in for Tom, can't she?

JOE. Of course, it's alright Fadge, and with the compensation we can hire someone to work the lights and sell the tickets. It's alright. I'm delighted for you both. Really I am.

ALL. We all are, *etc.*

TERRY. This whole Christmas is like a fairytale.

HENRY. Bloody nightmare more like.

TERRY. Shut up.

CARNFORTH. Oh Nina darling, just remembered there's a visitor for you out front.

ALL. Oooo!

Cut.

99   INT. CHURCH – NIGHT.

> *Empty auditorium save one man. All the actors come out after NINA, who stops a moment, peering into the semi-darkness.*

NINA. . . . Dad . . . ? DAD!

> *She runs towards him, tripping, of course, at the last bit and falling into his arms.*

NINA. I can't believe it, I can't believe you came, did you like it, did you?

DAD. You were wonderful.

> *She turns, the whole company are on the stage, drinks and party gear in hand. JOE at the front.*

NINA. Oh, Dad, this is my family. I mean my friends,they're all wonderful, I mean you'll meet them all, and this is . . . (*Indicating* JOE.) the most utterly . . .

JOE. Stupid . . .

NINA. Heroic man.

> *She runs to him. Hugs him. The company watch. Her Dad watches. This conversation is just for the two of them and all of them.*

NINA. I'm so proud of you.

JOE. Thank you, it isn't often you turn down life-long financial security and a great career.

NINA. Rubbish. You have a great career. And you have me.

JOE. Really?

NINA. If you'd like.

HENRY. Get his name on the dotted line love. He's a shifty git.

> VERNON *switches the music on.*

NINA. Would you like to dance?

JOE. I thought you didn't dance?

NINA. I thought better of it (*They start to dance slowly.*) and I reckon if I play my cards right I might get my leg over tonight.

JOE. I'm not just a fabulously attractive sex object you know.

NINA. Yes you are.

JOE. Fair enough. Won't your Dad be rather appalled at this?

NINA. Oh he knows all about you. Check out his phone bill. I think he's just accepted his last reverse charge call from me.

> *Around them everyone's starting to dance.* TOM *with* FADGE, MOLLY *with* VERNON, HENRY *with* TERRY, *and* CARNFORTH, *a bit pissed, with* NINA's DAD.

CARNFORTH. Actors: they're all the same aren't they?

DAD. This is marvellous.

JOE. You know, despite my immense purity of soul and being cleansed by my art, I'm still always going to get depressed and mad.

NINA. Well we can get depressed together, that's fun.

JOE. Are you always going to be optimistic?

NINA. No, I'm going to be miserable and fat and get a huge saggy ass.

JOE. Mmmm lovely. I can just feel it starting actually . . .

> *Cut.*

100   EXT. CHURCH – NIGHT.

> *The midnight bell strikes.*

NINA O/S. Listen everyone, Merry Christmas.

ALL O/S. Merry Christmas!

> *We fade to black. As the credits start, a beautiful rendition of the hymn 'In The Bleak Midwinter' begins.*
>
> *The end.*

Assistant Director	Simon Moseley
Camera Operator	Trevor Coop
Sound Mixer	Peter Glossop
Script Supervisor	Anna Worley
Chief Make-up/Hair	Jenny Shircore
Property Buyer	Celia Bobak
2nd Assistant Director	Emma Pounds
Gaffer Electrician	Ken Pettigrew
Location Manager	Tom White
Production Accountant	John Sargent
1st Assistant Editor	Daniel Farrell
2nd Assistant Editor	Robbie Broughton
Sound Editor	Richard Fettes
Assistant Sound Editor	Melanie Viner Cuneo
Focus Pullers	Nick Penn
	Simon Finney
Clapper Loader	Skip Margetts
Grip	Darren Quinn
Camera Trainee	Marc Atherfold
Grips Assistant	Michael Cuming
Boom Operator	Clive Fleury
Sound Assistant	Tom Glossop
Re-Recording Mixers	Robin O'Donoghue
	Dominic Lester
Re-Recording Facility	Twickenham Film Studios
Foley Recorded by	Delta Sound Services
Foley Mixer	Ed Colyer
Foley Editor	Gerard McCann
Dialogue Editor	Jim Roddan
Assistant Dialogue Editor	Kevin Ahern
Editing Trainee	Jens Baylis
Music Recorded at	Air Edel Recording Studios
Music Engineers	Paul Hulme
	Tom Meadows

Make-up Artists	Ivana Primorac
	Christina Whitney
Miss Saunders Make-up	Joan Hills
Miss Collins Hair	Sally Harrison
Wardrobe Mistress	Caroline Kelly
Wardrobe Assistants	Claire Porter
	Geraldine Geraghty
Miss Collins Costumes by	Nicole Farhi
Miss Saunders Costume by	Betty Jackson
Assistant Art Director	Nic Pallace
Prop Master	Frank Billington Marks
Standby Props	Peter Grant
Best boy Electrician	Billy Merrell
Electricians	Tom O'Sullivan
	John Curtis
Fight Arranger	Nick Hall
Stunts	Chrissie Monk
Skating Coach	Nola Haynes
3rd Assistant Directors	Matthew Penry-Davey
	Emma Griffiths
Production Assistants	Sally Ross
	Rebecca Ciallella
Stagehand	Michael Cohen
Painter	Peter Mounsey
Riggers	Alf Newvell
	Ian Rolfe
Publicity	Corbett and Keene
Stills	David Appleby
Transport Captain	Terry Pritchard
Unit Drivers	Mike Bevan
	Paul Gamby
Title Design	Simon Giles
	Alan Church
Payroll Services	Sargent Disc Ltd
Fire Protection	Sec Fire and Rescue Ltd
Health and Safety	Brian Shemmings
Unit Nurse	Anne Casey

Catering Services by	First Choice Location Services Ltd
Location Transport	D & D International Ltd
Facilities	Location Facilities

Lighting Equipment	Lee Lighting Ltd
Processing and Prints	Rank Film Laboratories Ltd
Laboratory Supervisor	Ray Adams
Opticals	The Magic Camera Company
Editing Equipment	Edit Hire Ltd

Lenses and Panaflex Camera by Panavision

Originated on Eastman Film from Kodak Dolby Stereo DigitaL

'Mule Train' (Lange, Heath, Glickman) copyright 1949
Bulls Eye Music Inc. USA, used by permission of Campbell
Connelly & Co. Ltd. London.

'Heart of Glass' (Deborah Harry & Chris Stein)
published by Chrysalis Music Inc.

With Special Thanks to

Michael Redding, Danny Hunter, Angel And Bermans,
Julian MacCloud, Phil Turner, Paul Olliver, Ron Pearce,
Hugh Whittaker, Peter MacCrimmon, Robin O'Donoghue,
Gerry Humphries, Dennis Bartlett, Peter Gundry, Ben Elton,
Special Treats, Richard Bonneville, Billy Hinshelwood,
Maggie Rodford and Michael J. Smith.

Filmed on Location and at Shepperton Studios, Shepperton,
London, England.